EIGHT
SCIENCE FICTION
PLAYS

THE **G**LOBE **R**EADER'S **C**OLLECTION

EIGHT SCIENCE FICTION PLAYS

GLOBE FEARON EDUCATIONAL PUBLISHER
A Division of Simon & Schuster
Upper Saddle River, New Jersey

Executive Editor: Barbara Levadi
Senior Editor: Bernice Golden
Editors: Helene Avraham, Laura Baselice, Robert McIlwaine
Editorial Assistant: Kristen Shepos
Product Development: PubWorks, Inc.
Production Manager: Penny Gibson
Senior Production Editor: Linda Greenberg
Production Editor: Walt Niedner
Marketing Manager: Sandra Hutchison
Electronic Page Production: The Wheetley Company, Inc.
Cover Design: The Wheetley Company, Inc.
Cover Art: Diana Ong's *Embryo* SuperStock, Inc.
Illustration: Lydia Halverson

Printed in the United States of America
1 2 3 4 5 6 7 8 9 10 99 98 97 96 95

ISBN: 0-8359-1361-9

GLOBE FEARON EDUCATIONAL PUBLISHER
A Division of Simon & Schuster
Upper Saddle River, New Jersey

CONTENTS

READING
SCIENCE FICTION
PLAYS

Most fiction is about the world as we know it. It's as if the writer held up a mirror to life. In the reflection, we see how people act. We see the laws of nature as we are used to seeing them.

Some writers enjoy presenting other worlds. They use their knowledge of science to spur their imaginations. They create worlds that one day might exist.

The plays you are about to read are *science fiction*. They are made-up stories based on scientific ideas. In some, such as *The Seven Sisters*, the ideas are almost within the reach of scientists now. A few plays, such as *The Green Computer*, provide a warning. They show what can happen when science moves too far or too quickly. All of the plays offer a thrilling escape from reality. They are out of this world!

How to Read a Play

Imagine people sitting blindfolded in a theater. They would see neither the stage settings nor the actors. Such an audience would have to rely only on what it could hear. The costumes, the actors' gestures, and the expressions on their faces would not be appreciated.

When you read the plays in this book, don't be blindfolded. Keep your eyes and ears open. Even when you read silently, try to make a picture of the stage in your mind's eye. Here are some ways to help you train and use your imagination.

1. Stage Setting When the curtain goes up and the play begins, you have a stage setting before you. The playwright uses *stage directions* to describe the set and physical actions of the actors for you. These stage directions are usually printed on the page in *italics*. Think about the stage set as if you were visiting a new place for the first time. What are your first impressions? What kind of people live here? What sort of action might take place here?

The stage direction below is from the last act of *The Green Computer*. Note how it increases the atmosphere of strangeness established in the first act. Also note how it shows the "character" of the computer.

> *The Molecular Computing Room. The walls are lined with all types of computer instruments, flashing lights, knobs, and computer tape machines and circular tape heads. A digital army clock reads 1203 hours. On the wall next to the clock is a plaque that states in large letters, "SITE OF THE FIRST LIVING COMPUTER." Alex sits behind a huge green keyboard and an eerie green computer screen, under a gigantic hanging sweet-potato plant. He looks up as Ed runs in, out of breath, followed by Marsha.*

2. Exposition The beginning of a play suddenly plunges you into other people's lives. You will naturally have questions about these people. Who are they? What are their relationships to one another? What are their problems? How did these problems happen? You can usually answer these questions in several ways. One is by reading the dialogue carefully. *Dialogue* is the conversation between the people in a play.

For example, what do you learn from the opening dialogue in *Only Slightly Different?* This conversation shows you that Zack and Kyrie have just arrived at a space pod circling the moon. Both of these young people are well informed about space technology. Both are excited about their futures. We also discover that Kyrie is rather lonely. She looks forward to having a close friend. These facts are part of the play's *exposition*, or background.

3. Characters The people in a play are called its *characters*. Your first impression of them often comes from what you *see*, not what you *hear*. The characters' surroundings may tell you something important before a single word is spoken. For example, take a look at the family breakfast scene in *Jupiter Park*. The year is 2222. Tiny computer screens float above the table. Food simply appears from behind a sliding wall panel. Clearly, this is the world of the future.

As the play unfolds, you learn more about the characters' relationships. Close attention should be paid to what they say to each other and how they act around each other. To understand a character better, focus on his or her needs and goals.

In *A Clash of Wills*, we see the two laser sword fighters in separate scenes with their doctors. The atmosphere on Tia's planet Bast is grim and businesslike. There is no humor on Bast.

> **Doctor:** (inserting microshields on Tia's shoulders) *I cannot imagine the lack of skills of doctors on Dole. They don't start training until they've completed 13 youth years! I was programmed to be a doctor before I was born and have received medical*

training since I was three. . . .

TIA: *So they live on some worthless little moon, do they? They disgust me!*

This is in stark contrast to the discussion in the doctor's office on Dole:

DOCTOR: (inserting a microshield at each shoulder) *Nor does it take training from the age of three to be a good doctor.*

STONE: *What do you mean?*

DOCTOR: *On Bast, children are taken from their mothers at age three to begin their training in a field chosen for them by Bast's rulers.*

STONE: *That's unfair! Children need to be around people who love them. . . .*

From the characters, you sense that the fight between Tia and Stone will be a battle of skills and ideas.

4. Plot The events that happen in a play are called the *plot*. These events are not random. One event leads logically to another, forming the action. The action is always built around a problem or struggle. This is called a *conflict*.

There are several different kinds of conflict in the plays you are about to read. For example, a play can show an outer conflict. In *Tendar Fever*, the two scientists, Stacey and Voni, must struggle against the spreading epidemic. They also must deal with the rising fear and panic that have driven the threatened population to riot and mob rule.

Finally, a play can show a struggle within an individual. Tia is faced with an inner conflict in *A Clash of Wills*. She must choose between two very different points of view. Will she choose loyalty and self-denial? Or will she choose to be herself and enjoy freedom of thought?

Keep conflict in mind as you read the plays in this book. Watch for situations in which characters have both outer and inner conflicts. Kyrie in *Only Slightly Different* is an example. She wants to have a friend exactly like herself. She also knows it is wrong to change someone.

There are some questions to ask about conflict as the action unfolds. What are the characters struggling against? What are they struggling for? Is the main character fighting for a goal, for an ideal, or for life itself?

The conflicts in a play finally reach a point of greatest tension. This is called the *climax*. The climax of a play is a turning point. The main character must make an important decision or take a decisive action. This action usually resolves the conflicts and leads directly to the conclusion.

The climax in *The Seven Sisters* comes 14 years after the beginning of the play. One of the girls recognizes a group of small, carved, animal figurines. The thing is that she has never seen it before. In a moment, one mystery is solved and another is created. This is the play's turning point.

See if you can find the climax of the other plays in this book. If you can pick out the main character, focus on his or her needs and goals. Discover the moment of crisis in a play. Remember: These plays are *science fiction*. They can't really happen—not today, anyway.

Star-Joy

Jeffrey Cooper

Have you ever looked up into the night sky and wondered whether there is intelligent life out there? The sky is filled with countless planets and stars like our sun. Some scientists believe that some form of intelligent life may be out there.

Many UFOs, or Unidentified Flying Objects, have been reported. Some people claim to have seen spaceships from another planet. Others say that they have been taken aboard these spaceships. Many of these claims have turned out to be hoaxes. Others have remained "unidentified."

In the play you are about to read, Jean and Eliot Foster say that they have been contacted by aliens. They believe they can prove it, too. Newspaper reporter Tom Yamaguchi has been assigned to cover the Foster's story. Yamaguchi is determined to discover the truth. He wants to know if we are alone in the universe—or not.

VOCABULARY WORDS

fascinated (FAS-uh-nay-tehd) strongly attracted or interested
❖ Most people are *fascinated* by moving objects in space.

journalism (JER-nuh-lihz-uhm) newspaper or magazine writing
❖ Marcy had years of experience in *journalism* before she wrote her own column.

encounter (ihn-KOWN-tuhr) meeting
❖ The movie we watched was about an *encounter* with creatures from outer space.

publicity (puh-BLIHS-uh-tee) public attention
❖ Everyone thought the inventor would seek *publicity*.

superstition (soo-per-STIH-shuhn) belief based on ignorance, fear, or trust in magic
❖ It is an ancient *superstition* that the number 13 is unlucky.

KEY WORD

UFO Unidentified Flying Object
❖ Some observers were convinced that the *UFO* was just an airplane.

CHARACTERS

Tom Yamaguchi, *a journalist*
Jean Foster, *a woman in her late fifties*
Eliot Foster, *Jean's husband*
Maria, *Tom's editor*

SETTING

Act One
Scene 1
The newsroom of a small Midwestern newspaper
Scene 2
The living room of Jean and Eliot Foster
Act Two
Scene 1
The news room, following day
Scene 2
The desert at night, one week later

ACT ONE, SCENE 1

*T**he newsroom of a small-town** newspaper somewhere in the Midwest. In the center of the stage is a desk with a computer and a telephone on it. Tom Yamaguchi enters, carrying a cup of coffee. He sits at the desk and turns on the computer. After punching a few keys, he leans back in his chair to read the screen. It is clear from his expression that he is unhappy with what he sees.*

TOM: This must be some kind of bad joke!

(He stands and paces for a moment before resuming his seat. Then he takes a sip of coffee and dials a number on the telephone.)

Maria? Tom Yamaguchi here. . . . Fine, thanks. Sounds like you've still got that nasty cold. . . . I hope so, too. Anyway, I was just checking my messages—Yes, I did. That's what I wanted to talk to you about. . . . Actually, I think it's a *terrible* idea for a story. . . . Of course people are fascinated by UFOs. They're fascinated by Santa Claus and the Easter Bunny, too, but that doesn't mean we have to run serious pieces on them in the *Post*. . . . I understand what you're saying, Maria. I enjoy a good science fiction story as much as the next guy. It's just that— Really? A top secret government document?. . . Well, that doesn't mean it's true, does it?

(He stands again and paces in front of his desk while talking.)

Just because people *think* they've been inside a flying saucer doesn't mean—Anyway, people are tired of stories about people being snatched up by little green creatures in flying saucers. And if they want to read that kind of garbage, they don't go looking for it in a serious newspaper like the *Post*. . . . No, I'm not trying to tell you how to do your job. I'm just—Of *course* you're still the boss, Maria. No one's questioning that. All I'm saying is—

(A long pause. He flops down into his seat with a defeated air.)

Okay, fine. If that's the way you want it. We'll run a front-page story on some loony couple who think they had lunch with E.T. . . . What do you mean *attitude*? I don't have any attitude. In fact, the more I think about it, the more I think this would make a terrific human interest piece for the Sunday supplement. Why don't you call Bob Rosen over at the magazine desk and—That's very nice of you to say, but I really don't think I'm the right person for this particular—This afternoon? Hold on a second. *(He checks his computer.)* I was planning to get some work done on that budget-crisis story. Why?. . . You what?

(Agitated, he jumps up and knocks over his coffee cup. Opening a desk drawer, he pulls out some napkins and begins to mop up coffee from the floor as he continues to talk.)

I really wish you'd let me check my calendar before you go and set up appointments for me, Maria. It just so happens—All right, all right. I'll be there.

(He stops mopping long enough to write in his notepad.)

I got it. One o'clock. No problem. . . . Yeah, you have a good one too, boss. And take care of that cold. You sound awful!

(He hangs up the phone and, looking disgusted, dumps the soggy napkins in the wastebasket.)

Fifteen years in journalism, and I'm still working the UFO beat. And people ask me why I love the newspaper business!

(The stage goes dark.)

ACT ONE, SCENE 2

The living room of Jean and Eliot Foster. The Fosters sit together on an overstuffed sofa. Tom, notepad and pen in hand, sits on a chair facing them.

JEAN: Are you sure you wouldn't like a cup of tea, Mr. Yamaguchi?

TOM: I'm sure, Mrs. Foster.

JEAN: Eliot and I always drink herb tea. We find that caffeine in the evening keeps us from falling asleep.

TOM: Come to think of it, a cup of strong black coffee might be just what I need.

JEAN: I'll get you a cup. *(She leaves.)*

ELIOT: I get the feeling you're not too keen on being here, Mr. Yamaguchi.

TOM: To tell you the truth, Mr. Foster, I'm not much of a believer in UFOs.

ELIOT: Can't say as I blame you, Mr. Yamaguchi. *(He stands up and extends his hand.)* Thanks for stopping by.

TOM: *(startled)* That's it? You're not going to try to convince me?

ELIOT: Nope. Frankly, I'd just as soon no one else knew what happened to Jean and me out on the hill that afternoon. The only reason we told anyone in the first place was Jean figured we had a patriotic duty to report it to the government.

TOM: *(with mock seriousness)* That's very responsible of you.

ELIOT: *(continuing as though he has not heard the remark)* If I'd have known the newspapers were going to get a hold of the story, I'd never have told a soul.

TOM: *(writing in his notepad)* Let me see if I've got this straight. You think you had a close encounter with some little green creatures from outer space, and you don't even want to talk to anybody about it?

ELIOT: *(amused)* I hate to ruin your fun, Mr. Yamaguchi, but there weren't any little green creatures. And, yes, I'd really prefer not to talk about it. The only reason Jean and I agreed to talk to *you* is that someone must have read that secret report somehow and leaked it to the press. We knew some reporter or another would be showing up around here sooner or later, and we figured it might as well be you.

TOM: Why me?

(Jean enters and hands a cup of coffee to Tom.)

JEAN: We've been reading your articles in the *Post* for years, Mr. Yamaguchi. You're a fine writer. When we got the call from that editor of yours—What's her name, dear?

ELIOT: Maria-something, I think.

JEAN: That's it. When Maria-something called, we said we'd only talk to the *Post* if she'd send Tom Yamaguchi. We figured that if anyone could tell our story without making us sound like a couple of crazy old fools, it would be you.

TOM: I'm flattered.

ELIOT: Frankly, Mr. Yamaguchi, I don't think your Maria-something was too thrilled about sending you.

TOM: No?

ELIOT: Apparently, she didn't think you'd believe us, and it looks as if she was right. *(He turns to his wife.)* Mr. Yamaguchi was just leaving.

TOM: *(He looks at his watch and takes a sip of coffee.)* I have a little time before my next appointment, Mr. Foster. I suppose I may as well hear your story, as long as I'm here anyway.

ELIOT: *(shrugging)* Up to you.

TOM: Please. *(He gestures toward the sofa, and the Fosters sit down. Tom turns to a fresh page in his notepad.)* Why don't you start by telling me exactly where you were when you first saw the little green . . . UFO.

JEAN: It was just a few months ago. It was a beautiful Saturday afternoon, so Eliot and I decided to have a picnic lunch out on Cumberland Hill. Have you ever been out there?

TOM: Can't say as I have.

JEAN: A lovely spot for a romantic picnic. Are you a married man, Mr. Yamaguchi?

TOM: No, I'm not.

JEAN: That's too bad. *(She takes Eliot's hand and smiles at him.)* The universe must feel like an awfully unfriendly place when you think you're all alone.

ELIOT: I don't think that Mr. Yamaguchi is interested in hearing our thoughts about marriage, Jean.

JEAN: Oh, but I wasn't talking about—

ELIOT: Jean.

JEAN: I'm sorry. I was rambling again, wasn't I?

TOM: That's all right, Mrs. Foster. You were saying?

JEAN: *(to Eliot)* Where was I, dear?

ELIOT: Cumberland Hill.

JEAN: Yes. Cumberland Hill. Eliot and I were enjoying our picnic—

ELIOT: *(gazing lovingly at his wife)* Jean makes the most wonderful deviled eggs.

TOM: I'm sure she does.

JEAN: Anyway, to make a long story short, Eliot thought he saw something glowing in the distance. He went off to see what it was. I followed him to the edge of the hill.

ELIOT: And that's where we saw it.

JEAN: We both saw it.

TOM: *It* being the UFO?

ELIOT: Well, I don't know if you could call it an unidentified *flying* object. It was more like a hovering object, sort of hanging in space at the edge of the hill.

JEAN: I'm not exactly sure you could call it an *object* at all. It was more like a very bright light, except that you could look directly at it without hurting your eyes.

TOM: Did it occur to you at this point that your eyes might have been playing tricks on you?

JEAN: Well . . . no, it didn't.

TOM: Or that you were seeing some sort of reflection?

ELIOT: Well, I wondered for a minute. That is, until the thing spoke to us.

TOM: It spoke to you?

JEAN: Well, not exactly *spoke*. It seemed more as if someone—or something—were thinking to us.

ELIOT: Or *through* us.

TOM: You heard someone thinking?

ELIOT: Sounds crazy, doesn't it? If Jean hadn't been there, I might not have believed it myself.

TOM: *(writing in his notepad)* Then what happened?

JEAN: Then we went inside.

ELIOT: At least we *think* we were inside. It was kind of hard to tell. Everything after the blue light was like some kind of wonderful dream.

TOM: The blue light?

JEAN: From the glowing sphere. There were two beams, actually. One for each of us.

ELIOT: Drawing us in. They seemed to shoot out of the sphere.

JEAN: It was very nice. Very welcoming. *(She looks at her husband and smiles.)*

ELIOT: Next thing we knew, there we were.

TOM: And where exactly *were* you?

JEAN: Everywhere.

ELIOT: Or maybe nowhere. It's hard to say.

TOM: And then?

ELIOT: And then we remember being held—

JEAN: More like *hugged*—

ELIOT: Yes, hugged by these hands—

JEAN: Not *hands* exactly—

ELIOT: No, not hands exactly, but very gentle and very strong at the same time. There was this marvelous feeling of being loved and cared for, like a baby must feel when its mother washes it in warm water and pats it dry with a soft, fluffy towel.

JEAN: Or maybe how it feels before it's born.

TOM: So these hands made you feel safe and secure?

JEAN: It was more than that. It was like nothing either of us had ever felt before.

ELIOT: It was star-joy. That's what it was, all right.

TOM: Star-joy?

JEAN: That's the only word we could think of to describe it. It's this warm, comfortable feeling—

ELIOT: —this absolute *knowing*—

JEAN: —that everything in the world—

ELIOT: —everything in the *universe*—

JEAN: —is happening exactly the way it's supposed to happen.

TOM: *(skeptically)* Don't worry, be happy?

ELIOT: We know it sounds ridiculous, but it sure didn't *feel* ridiculous.

JEAN: It's a good feeling, Mr. Yamaguchi. A feeling you know you're never going to forget, no matter how long you live.

TOM: I'm sure it is, Mrs. Foster.

JEAN: *(to her husband)* He doesn't understand.

17

ELIOT: *(to his wife)* He wasn't there. He wasn't chosen.

TOM: What happened next? After these hands, or whatever they were, examined you.

JEAN: The next thing either of us remembers is being back at our picnic blanket, eating deviled eggs.

ELIOT: Jean makes the best deviled eggs.

TOM: And?

JEAN: We finished eating and went home.

ELIOT: The next day, we called that Air Force base outside of Greendale and told them what happened to us.

TOM: And that's it? That's the whole story?

ELIOT: Pretty much.

JEAN: Sounds kind of crazy, doesn't it?

TOM: Frankly, Mrs. Foster, it sounds *more* than a little crazy.

ELIOT: I suppose it would to you.

TOM: *(ignoring the remark)* Even if there *were* such things as flying saucers—which I still don't believe for a minute—why would they choose people like *you* to show themselves to? Why wouldn't they reveal themselves to world leaders or great scientists or—

ELIOT: Newspaper reporters, maybe?

TOM: Maybe. I'll tell you one thing, Mr. Foster. If I ever had the kind of experience you folks say that you have had, I sure wouldn't go on living my life just like nothing special ever happened. You'd be seeing my face on every talk show in the country. The book

I'd write would be sure to win me the Pulitzer Prize. I've been hoping for that prize since the day I signed up for journalism school.

ELIOT: Maybe that's the whole point, Mr. Yamaguchi. Maybe that's why they choose folks like Jean and me to show themselves to—folks who feel like they already have pretty near everything they ever wanted out of life in the first place.

JEAN: Folks who figure that the star-joy is more than enough of a prize all by itself.

TOM: *(He stands up and walks over to the window. He gazes out in silence for a long moment before speaking.)* I'm going to be frank with you folks. You seem like very nice people, and I sure don't want to hurt anybody's feelings. . . .

ELIOT: But?

TOM: But nothing you've told me proves that you've been anywhere or done anything out of the ordinary. Do you have any pictures of this glowing sphere?

ELIOT: Didn't think to bring along a camera on our picnic.

JEAN: Had we known we would be seeing the sphere, we might very well have brought one along. Eliot is a marvelous photographer.

TOM: Well, did you bring anything back from the alien ship?

JEAN: You mean like a souvenir?

TOM: Anything!

JEAN: It just didn't seem important at the time.

19

ELIOT: There *is* the star-joy, of course. We didn't have *that* before they let us inside.

TOM: Listen, folks. I'm very happy for you. It sounds like you had a wonderful time, and I'm glad everything turned out all right for you. But there's just no story here.

ELIOT: That's up to you, Mr. Yamaguchi. As I said, we're not looking for any publicity. You can go back to Maria what's-her-name and tell her we turned out to be another crazy old couple who think they saw a flying saucer.

TOM: I wouldn't say that. *(He closes his notepad.)* I'll just tell her there's still no proof that aliens ever landed on Cumberland Hill.

(He shakes hands with Mr. Foster.)

JEAN: Of course, there is the matter of the finger.

ELIOT: I thought we weren't going to bring that up, Jean.

JEAN: I know, dear, but Mr. Yamaguchi came all this way to talk to us. It seems a shame to send him back with nothing to write about.

TOM: What's this about a finger?

JEAN: It's his pinkie. The one on his right hand.

TOM: *(looking at Eliot's hand, which he is still clasping)* What about it? It looks perfectly normal to me.

ELIOT: That's the strange thing.

(He releases Tom's hand and holds up his right pinkie.)

JEAN: You see, Mr. Yamaguchi, Eliot lost a pinkie just

like that one in a threshing machine more than forty
years ago.

(The stage goes dark.)

ACT TWO, SCENE 1

*Tom sits at his desk in the newsroom. He is talking on
the telephone.*

TOM: I know what I said, Maria, but everything's different now. I *have* to follow up on this one. . . . I don't
care what Tony Robinson says. This story is too big
for the Sunday supplement. For all I know, it may be
too big for this *newspaper*. . . . All right. So how do
you explain this business with the finger?. . . Of
course I checked it out. It's *true*, Maria. Eliot Foster
lost his pinkie in an accident on his uncle's farm
when he was a teenager. I even saw the hospital
records. Besides, all his neighbors swear the man
was missing his right pinkie until a few months
ago. . . . No, I can't explain how a pinkie can grow
back overnight. That's why I'm staying with this
story until I find out exactly what happened to the
Fosters on Cumberland Hill. . . . I agree with you.
The part about the blue light is straight out of some
bad science fiction movie. And that business with the
hands and the—what did they call it?. . . Right. The
star-joy? Sounds like a lot of nonsense to me. Still, I
keep coming back to that finger. . . . No, I don't think
they are crazy.

(He shows more excitement.)

They sure were happy, though. If somebody ever bot-
tles that star-joy stuff, they're going to make a million

bucks! . . . I don't care if the *Post* pays for it or not. I've got to go and find out for myself.

(He stands and shifts his weight from foot to foot.)

Maybe I'm as crazy as the Fosters. But when a guy suddenly grows back a finger after he thinks he was visited by aliens, I figure maybe there's a story in it. So when the Fosters told me that the glowing sphere is going to land in the middle of Utah next Thursday, I knew I had to be there. . . . I have no idea how they know. *They* don't even know how they know. But they told me exactly where and when the landing is going to take place. . . . Of *course* I checked it out. It's in the middle of the desert, a couple of miles off the highway. . . . Two in the morning. . . . No, I've never been to the desert in the middle of the night before. . . . I'm sure it will be. So I'll bring along an extra sweater.

(He sits down.)

Don't worry so much, Maria. I can take care of myself. . . . Are you kidding? Who would be crazy enough to join me on a trip like this? I'm going to Utah to wait for the spaceship to land in the desert in the middle of the night so I can write a story for the *Post* and maybe win myself a Pulitzer Prize. Want to come along?. . . You *would*?. . . No, I'd love the company. I just can't believe you're really interested. . . . Of *course* I could use a good photographer. I may be the world's greatest reporter, but I take terrible snapshots. But are you sure you want to . . . Okay, Maria. You're the boss. You can even drive the first ten hours if you want to. Just try to get rid of that cold by Thursday, okay? We wouldn't want to infect any little green creatures.

(Tom hangs up. He is gazing thoughtfully at his right pinkie as the stage slowly fades to black.)

ACT TWO, SCENE 2

It is night in the desert. Tom and Maria sit on beach chairs, their backpacks and a thermos bottle beside them on the sand. Maria has a couple of cameras around her neck. She sneezes loudly into a large handkerchief.

TOM: Bless you.

MARIA: What does that mean, anyway? Why do people say "bless you" when somebody sneezes?

TOM: Who knows? Some old superstition, I guess. People believe in a lot of weird things.

MARIA: Like flying saucers?

TOM: Hey! You're the one who wanted to come along for the ride.

MARIA: I know. It's not your fault that I'm freezing in some stupid desert in the middle of the night waiting for a UFO to touch down.

TOM: I never imagined it could get so cold in the desert.

MARIA: *(after a long pause)* What time is it, anyway?

TOM: Ten minutes later than the last time you asked. Why? You got a late date?

MARIA: Yeah. With a little green man from outer space. He was supposed to be here a couple of hours ago.

TOM: What can I tell you? You know how those little green guys are. *(He stands up and begins to pace back*

23

and forth, hugging his shoulders to keep warm. He gazes at the sky.) Have you ever seen so many stars in your whole life?

MARIA: *(not looking up)* Yeah, about an hour ago. Also the hour before that, and the hour before that. . . .

TOM: I get your point. *(He sits down.)* Are we really out of coffee?

MARIA: *(sarcastically)* No, Tom. I just thought it would be terribly amusing to let you think we're stranded in this freezing desert without any hot coffee to keep us from turning into human popsicles. Don't I have a delicious sense of humor?

TOM: We're not really stranded, you know. The car's just a couple of miles back on the main road. We can head back toward civilization anytime we want to.

MARIA: Are you ready to turn back?

TOM: Are you?

MARIA: I asked you first.

TOM: What are we? A couple of seven-year-olds? Just tell me if you've had enough.

MARIA: Are you ready to admit that the Fosters never really saw a UFO?

TOM: As soon as you can explain how Eliot Foster's right pinkie grew back.

MARIA: I'm sure there's a perfectly—

(She jumps up and points toward the audience.)

MARIA: What's that?

TOM: Where? I don't see anything.

MARIA: That glow. It's beautiful! I've never seen anything so bright!

TOM: *(frantically gazing out into the audience)* What glow? What are you talking about?

MARIA: Oh, Tom! I think they're going to choose me!

TOM: Who? Who's going to choose you?

(Suddenly, the stage goes dark except for a blue spotlight on Maria. She holds her arms out in a gesture of welcome, a look of pure joy on her face. Then the blue light is gone. When the lights come back on, Tom is standing alone, staring at the spot where Maria was last seen.) Maria? MARIA? *(He bustles around the stage in search of Maria. Suddenly, she appears behind him, a blissful smile on her face. Her cameras are gone. Tom turns and sees her.)* Maria! Are you all right?

MARIA: I'm all right, Tom. Everything is all right. We can go home now.

TOM: What do you mean, we can go home? What happened to you? One minute you were standing there, and the next minute—

MARIA: *(She smiles and places her hands gently on his shoulders.)* It's all right, Tom. Trust me. Everything's just perfect.

TOM: What did you see? Did you take any pictures? *(He pulls back.)* What happened to your cameras?

MARIA: Don't worry about the cameras, Tom. Don't worry about anything.

TOM: I don't understand this, Maria. Please tell me what's going on!

MARIA: There's nothing to tell, Tom. I'm sorry you weren't chosen. If you'd been there, you'd know.

TOM: Know *what*? Did you see the sphere? Did you go inside? Why didn't *I* see anything?

MARIA: It's all right, Tom. You don't have to worry about aliens ever again. You were right. You should have been working on that budget story all along.

TOM: I don't care about the budget, Maria. I want to know what happened to you just now. And I want to know why it didn't happen to me!

MARIA: *(picking up her backpack and folding her beach chair)* I feel so good, Tom. In fact, I don't think I've ever felt better in my life. And did you notice?

TOM: Notice what?

MARIA: I don't even have a cold anymore. *(She picks up her chair and walks offstage.)*

TOM: Maria! Wait! *(He stares after her for a moment. Then he looks out toward the audience.)* Wait a minute, Maria! Is that it? *(He points.)* Maria! I think they came back for me! *(He holds out his arms in a gesture of welcome. He closes his eyes and waits. Nothing happens. After a long moment, he opens his eyes and slowly lowers his arms. Then, with an air of profound disappointment, he folds up his beach chair and picks up his backpack and cooler. He takes one last look around before slowly walking off stage. The silence is broken a moment later by the harsh sound of Tom's loud sneeze.)*

MARIA: *(offstage)* Bless you.

READING FOR UNDERSTANDING

The following paragraphs summarize the play. Decide which of the words below the paragraph best fits in each blank. Some words are used more than once. Write your answers on a separate sheet of paper.

Tom Yamaguchi worked for a **(1)**_____. When his editor asked him to do a story on **(2)**_____, he showed little interest. His editor, however, had already set up an appointment for him to meet with **(3)**_____. Even though Tom was not a believer in **(4)**_____, he asked the Fosters to tell their story. The Fosters told Tom that they had been enjoying a **(5)**_____ when they saw a **(6)**_____ in the distance. Mysterious **(7)**_____ spoke to them, and they were left with a feeling of absolute **(8)**_____. Tom wondered why aliens would show themselves to **(9)**_____ rather than to **(10)**_____. But when Mr. Foster showed Tom his **(11)**_____, which he claimed he had lost years ago, Tom knew he had a story.

Tom and Maria decided to go to the **(12)**_____ to wait for the **(13)**_____ to reappear. Suddenly, Maria saw a beautiful **(14)**_____, and she vanished. When she reappeared, Tom noticed her **(15)**_____ were missing. Maria had also lost her **(16)**_____.

Tom waited for the spaceship to return, but all he was left with was Maria's **(17)**_____ instead of the feeling that Mr. Foster had called **(18)**_____.

Words: *desert, scientists, the Fosters, pinkie, newspaper, cold, star-joy, spaceship, terror, UFOs, voices, cameras, glow, joy, picnic*

RESPONDING TO THE PLAY

1. If their report to the government had not been "leaked" to the newspaper, the Fosters never would have told anyone about the UFO. What would you do if you were Jean or Eliot Foster? Would you tell anyone about your experience? Who would you tell? What would you do if no one believed your story?

2. The events described in *Star-Joy* cannot be explained or proved, but they are interesting. What is your opinion about UFOs? Do you think that aliens have visited Earth, or do you think that reports of UFOs are nonsense? Explain your views in a paragraph.

REVIEWING VOCABULARY

1. A *superstition* is never based on **(a)** fear of the unknown **(b)** scientific evidence **(c)** a belief in magic.

2. A person who is *fascinated* by fish might find deep-sea diving **(a)** frightening **(b)** dull **(c)** exciting.

3. If you majored in *journalism* in college, you might **(a)** work in a nursery **(b)** start a newspaper **(c)** study UFOs.

4. A scientist who seeks *publicity* wants to **(a)** be recognized by the public **(b)** earn a lot of money **(c)** work with other scientists.

5. When Marie describes an *encounter* with an artist, she means a **(a)** friendship **(b)** disagreement **(c)** meeting.

THINKING CRITICALLY

1. When Tom meets the Fosters, he tells them he is "not much of a believer in UFOs." Should he have said that? If you were a reporter, how would you approach people who had an unusual story?

2. Mr. Foster says that Tom cannot understand the peace and happiness he and his wife felt because Tom was not "chosen." Why do you think aliens might choose certain people? Why do you think Tom was not chosen?

3. Tom feels that saying "Bless you" when someone sneezes is based on superstition. How does Tom feel about superstition? Why do you think some superstitions remain popular?

4. Explain what you think *star-joy* is. How does it seem to affect people?

WRITING PROJECTS

1. Imagine that you are Tom Yamaguchi. It is your job to write a feature article about the incident the Fosters described. In your article, include details from the play to give your readers a clear picture of what happened. Also, keep in mind Tom's reactions and opinions because you are writing the article from his point of view.

2. What if the aliens returned, this time to contact Tom? Add a scene to the play in which the aliens try to convince Tom to go with them to their home. How would the aliens try to persuade Tom? What would Tom's response be?

Only Slightly Different

Bruce Goldstone

How important is it for friends to be alike? How much should they have in common? Should friends have similar interests and opinions? Should they have the same hobbies? Is it important that friends also look alike?

In the play you are about to read, these questions are taken one step further. Four teenagers find themselves stranded together in space for one month.

Kyrie wants a friend who looks, acts, and thinks like her. Mila wants to be that friend. The question is: How far is Kyrie willing to go to create her idea of a perfect friend? As you read the play, think about whether you would have acted as Mila did if you found yourself in a similar situation.

VOCABULARY WORDS

simulation (sihm-yoo-LAY-shuhn) close imitation of a real-life action or device
❖ Airline pilots train in a *simulation* cockpit.

media (MEE-dee-uh) means of communication, such as TV, radio, and newspapers
❖ Politicians use the *media* to speak to the public.

metallic (muh-TAL-ihk) made of metal
❖ Would you like to have *metallic* hair?

genetic (juh-NEHT-ihk) having to do with genes
❖ People's eye color is *genetic*.

mutation (myoo-TAY-shuhn) change
❖ Due to a *mutation*, Lunarians have colorless eyes.

sterile (STEHR-uhl) free from germs
❖ Surgery demands *sterile* conditions.

spliced (splysd) joined by weaving together the end strands
❖ The engineer *spliced* the ends of the tape.

activates (AK-tuh-vayts) makes active; sets in motion
❖ This button *activates* the VCR's rewind function.

KEY WORDS

hypothalamus (hy-poh-THAL-uh-muhs) gland in the brain that regulates body functions
❖ The *hypothalamus* controls body temperature.

Dr. Frankenstein (FRAHNK-uhn-styn) creator of a monster
❖ There are many films about *Dr. Frankenstein*.

bioengineering (by-oh-ehn-juh-NIHR-ing) science that uses technology in biology and medicine
❖ Marina wants to major in *bioengineering*.

CHARACTERS

Zack, *seventeen years old, a human from Earth*
Kyrie, *sixteen years old, Zack's sister*
Mila, *sixteen years old, a Lunarian who lives on a moon
  colony*
Edo, *fourteen years old, Mila's brother*

SETTING

Act One
Scene 1
The command center

Scene 2
The biolab

Act Two
Scene 1
Mila's room

Scene 2
The biolab

Scene 3
Kyrie's room

Scene 4
The biolab

ACT ONE, SCENE 1

***T**he year 2162. The command center of
the Youth Pod of a satellite colony orbiting
the moon. This room contains all of the
controls that operate the Youth Pod. A very
complicated control panel is stage left; the
entry door is located upstage center. All of the walls are
metal or glass.*
  The entry door makes an electronic beep to signal that

it is opening. It opens, and Zack and Kyrie come into the room. They look around enthusiastically.

ZACK: Wow! Look at this place.

KYRIE: It looks just like the simulation pod back on Earth.

ZACK: I know, but somehow it's so much more real.

KYRIE: That's because it is real, Zack. Everything really works this time. Look—lights. *(Kyrie flicks a switch and a set of panel lights turn on.)* Stargazer. *(She flicks another switch and a screen turns on, showing space outside the capsule. She flicks it off again.)* Even the video hookup. *(She turns on a television, which faces away from the audience. The audience can hear the sound of the report in progress.)*

VIDEO: . . . due to the dramatically increasing populations of both Earth and the Lunar Colonies . . .

KYRIE: Hey listen, they're talking about us.

VIDEO: Population scientists predict that as much as twenty-five percent of our population will live in the orbiting satellite colonies before the year 2200. Later this afternoon, the first three families will assemble on the new satellite colony. They will live for one month on the new colony without interference from media or experts.

ZACK: At least they're going to leave us alone.

VIDEO: At the end of the month, they will assemble back on Earth to provide a full report of life in the new colony. The first inhabitants include the Mentons and their two children, Zack and Kyrie.

KYRIE: That's us! *(Kyrie points at the screen.)* Look, there you are.

VIDEO: Other inhabitants include the Bin family—

(Zack switches off the video monitor.)

KYRIE: Hey, why'd you turn that off?

ZACK: I'd rather be surprised.

KYRIE: Don't you want to know what they look like?

ZACK: We'll know soon enough.

KYRIE: We're going to be trapped on this pod for a month, and most of that time we'll be stuck in this stupid Youth Pod with four complete strangers. Aren't you even curious about what they're like?

ZACK: Of course I am. I'd just rather see them in person for the first time instead of on video. I'm sure they'll be interesting.

KYRIE: They better be. I want a friend, someone I can really talk to.

ZACK: I'm not surprised. The way you've been in bio training for the last five years, you've barely had a chance to meet anyone.

KYRIE: Everyone at that lab school was an idiot. I want a friend that's like me.

ZACK: Kyrie, nobody's like you.

KYRIE: Well then, I want someone close to me, OK?

(The entry door beeps again.)

ZACK: *(softly)* We'll know soon enough.

(Mila and Edo enter. They are Lunarians, with metallic

35

hair and fingernails. Their eyes have no color. Edo walks right up to Zack. Mila hangs back shyly.)

ZACK: Welcome to the Youth Pod.

EDO: Hi. I'm Edo. This is my sister, Mila.

ZACK: I'm Zack. This is my sister, Kyrie.

KYRIE: *(glum)* You're Lunarians.

EDO: You bet. *(He taps his fingernails on a metal desk, making a loud metallic clatter.)* See, we make great drummers.

ZACK: It's nice to meet you.

KYRIE: I thought you'd be humans.

EDO: That's funny, I thought you'd be friendly.

KYRIE: *(sharply)* Well at least my hair doesn't set off a metal detector.

EDO: No, but your brain might set off a dumb detector.

KYRIE: For your information, Mr. Lunarian, I happen to be practically a genius. I'm just one year away from my bioengineering degree.

EDO: Well, you act more like a brat.

ZACK: Hey, hey, hey, you two. There'll be plenty of time for fighting later. Hi, Mila, my name is Zack. And this is Kyrie.

KYRIE: Repeating it in case she didn't get it the first time?

MILA: What's her problem?

KYRIE: Her problem? Her problem is that she's stuck in an orbiting clam with a couple of Lunarians instead of real humans. *(sulky)* This isn't what I wanted at all.

EDO: Well, you're hardly what we were looking for, either.

KYRIE: I don't even want to look at you.

MILA: Well fine, if that's what you want. *(Mila runs out, choking back tears.)*

EDO: That's really nice, Kyrie. Thanks for the warm welcome. *(He goes out to comfort Mila. The door stays open.)* Mila! Mila!

ZACK: What's gotten into you, Kyrie?

KYRIE: I'm just disappointed is all. I wish they were humans.

ZACK: Well, they're not. So who cares? I don't see what difference it makes anyway.

KYRIE: I wanted a good friend. Someone I can share things with.

ZACK: So what? Don't you know what Lunarians are?

KYRIE: Of course I do. They're a race that evolved when humans first colonized the moon. The early pressure domes leaked and the resulting atmospheric changes created a genetic mutation in the first Lunar colonists.

ZACK: Exactly. A very *slight* genetic change. They're just like humans.

KYRIE: Except they're not. They're Lunarians. They have metal hair, metal fingernails, and no eyes.

ZACK: They have eyes; they just don't have any color.

KYRIE: I want my best friend to have eyes like mine.

ZACK: So Mila won't be your best friend. Just stop being such a baby and treat them with a little respect, OK?

(Edo and Mila come back in. Zack and Kyrie do not notice them at first.)

KYRIE: Well, the other family better be humans.

MILA: And I hope they're Lunarians.

EDO: Well, I hope they're kangaroos. Can we just drop this subject?

ZACK: Good idea, Edo. Let's look around.

EDO: This place sure looks familiar.

ZACK: You two must have had the same kind of training we did.

EDO: Yeah, back on the moon, we had a simulated training room that looked exactly like this.

ZACK: Only most of the switches weren't live, right?

EDO: Yeah, you'd flip a switch and nothing would happen. Just a computer message telling you what was *supposed* to happen.

KYRIE: I bet you don't know what most of them do anyway.

MILA: We do, too.

KYRIE: Oh yeah?

MILA: I know just as much about this pod as you do.

KYRIE: I doubt that very much.

MILA: *(daring Kyrie)* How do you raise the temperature here? *(Kyrie flips a switch; rows of heaters turn on.)*

KYRIE: *(daring Mila)* OK, how do you turn on the stargazer? *(Mila flips a switch on the main control panel. The outside monitor turns on.)*

MILA: I bet you can't arm the protective shield.

ZACK: Hey, you're not supposed to play with that.

KYRIE: I can too. *(She flips a series of switches. A red light flashes.)* See, it's armed now.

EDO: Stop this stupid game. You're both just too smart, OK?

KYRIE: I bet you can't move the connective tunnel.

MILA: *(hesitant)* The one that connects us to the main pod?

ZACK: That's enough, Kyrie.

KYRIE: See, she can't do it. She doesn't know how.

MILA: *(rashly)* I can too. See.

(A loud blasting sound is heard. The picture on the stargazer starts to change.)

ZACK: What was that?

EDO: *(pointing to the stargazer)* Look! Our pod is launching!

KYRIE: *(laughing)* You blew it, Mila. You launched our pod. I told you so.

ZACK: It's not funny, Kyrie. Now we're stranded.

(They all look at Mila. Kyrie laughs; Mila glares back at her. Lights out.)

ACT ONE, SCENE 2

The Biolab. The next day. The biolab has one large computer experiment station, downstage right. It includes a variety of scientific testing tools, such as glass flasks, a microscope, and a computer sample analyzer. Kyrie is working at the experiment station. Zack comes in.

ZACK: What are you doing in here?

KYRIE: I'm working, that's what. I might as well get some work done while we're stuck out here.

ZACK: Well, it's your fault—

KYRIE: It is not. Mila pushed the wrong buttons, not me. She's the one who launched us into orbit. She could have killed us.

ZACK: It's not that bad, and you know it. In one month, we'll reconnect with the main pod.

KYRIE: Yeah, but a whole month trapped with those Lunarians! The other kids won't even be able to get on board.

ZACK: You should give them a chance.

KYRIE: I don't have to.

ZACK: Well then, don't. But don't expect anyone to pay much attention to you.

KYRIE: That's fine by me. I'll just do my work in peace. I can get a lot done in a month.

ZACK: You're wasting your time in here, Kyrie. You know, there's more to learn about than bioengineering.

KYRIE: Oh shut up, and let me do my work.

(Zack leaves. Kyrie works at her lab experiment. Mila walks in; Kyrie doesn't notice. Mila walks up to her and startles her. Kyrie drops a test tube; it breaks.)

KYRIE: Look what you made me do.

MILA: I'm sorry. Here, let me help.

(In her hurry to pick up the broken glass, Mila cuts herself.)

KYRIE: Clumsy. Just get out of the way. *(Kyrie finishes cleaning up the glass.)* What do you want, anyway?

MILA: I just wanted to say I'm sorry about this. About getting us stranded.

KYRIE: *(sarcastic)* OK, OK, you said it. Very nice. Now leave me alone.

MILA: Why do you hate me so much?

KYRIE: *(avoiding the question)* Are you bleeding?

MILA: I cut myself on that glass.

KYRIE: Well, it's supposed to be sterile in here. *(Kyrie hands Mila a first-aid kit.)* Here, bandage yourself up.

MILA: Look, you're bleeding too.

KYRIE: Am I?

MILA: See, we're the same after all.

(Kyrie looks at the cuts on their hands and gets an idea. Her tone suddenly changes. She's friendly and intense.)

KYRIE: Hey, you know something, we could be.

MILA: What?

KYRIE: It just might work.

MILA: What?!

KYRIE: Come here. *(Kyrie takes Mila's hand and brings it to her lab table. She squeezes the cut finger to get a drop of Mila's blood.)*

MILA: OUCH! *(Kyrie places Mila's blood in the analyzer. Then she takes a drop of her own blood and does the same.)*

KYRIE: Look. This machine analyzes the DNA in blood samples. Here's your blood, and here's mine. See?

MILA: They look the same.

KYRIE: They are, almost. Because Lunarians were once humans, we have almost exactly the same DNA. See that one spot there? That's the only difference.

MILA: So?

KYRIE: So think about it. If we could replace that little tiny bit of your DNA, you'd be human.

MILA: But that's impossible.

KYRIE: No, it's not. It's what I've been working on. You can alter some genes. All I have to do is splice a bit of my DNA into yours. Then I inject the new gene into your arm, and it travels to your hypothalamus gland. Then your gland takes over and reproduces the new DNA. In a month or two, all of your old DNA would be changed. You'd be human.

MILA: You mean, I'd be *you*. I'd have your DNA.

KYRIE: No, only a tiny little bit. You'd still be you exactly, only slightly different.

MILA: Slightly different.

KYRIE: Haven't you ever wanted to be human?

MILA: Well, I never thought—

KYRIE: It could be fun.

MILA: It sounds dangerous. And what happens if I don't like being human?

KYRIE: You will. But anyway, I could always change you back.

MILA: You could?

KYRIE: Sure. I'll just keep your blood sample alive. That way, when we get back to the main pod, if you're unhappy, we'll just make you Lunarian again.

MILA: I should ask Edo.

KYRIE: No, don't ask him. Let's make it our secret. They don't have to know.

MILA: Well, they'll notice when my hair starts changing color.

KYRIE: That'll take ages. Think how long it takes hair to grow. Come on, just for a month.

MILA: I don't know.

KYRIE: You got us into this mess. At least let's have some fun while we're stranded.

MILA: And I can change back whenever I want?

KYRIE: Sure.

MILA: Well . . . OK.

KYRIE: *(happily pointing to the blood samples)* We'll be real blood sisters!

MILA: That's right! Blood sisters!

(Lights out.)

ACT TWO, SCENE 1

One week later. Mila's room. A small, modern room, equipped with bed, side table, desk with computer, and a closet. Mila is asleep. There is a knock on the door.

MILA: *(stretching)* Kyrie, is that you? Come in.

(Kyrie comes in, peppy.)

KYRIE: Good morning. How's the hair? *(Kyrie inspects the roots of Mila's hair.)*

MILA: What do you think?

KYRIE: I think it's working! Look—it's turning brown instead of silver!

MILA: Are you sure?

KYRIE: And look at your fingernails! Down here at the edges.

MILA: This is incredible. What about my eyes?

KYRIE: Let me see. *(Mila bats her eyelashes like a silent-film star.)* Be still. I can't tell. Maybe they'll be blue.

MILA: Or purple.

KYRIE: Well, let's hope they turn a normal human color.

MILA: Yes, I've never dreamed of having orange eyes.

(The girls are laughing. Edo and Zack are passing by. They hear the laughing and walk in.)

ZACK: Well, look at you two.

EDO: For two people who hated each other at first sight, you've sure become good friends.

KYRIE: Oh, Mila's not so bad—now.

ZACK: What do you mean, now?

KYRIE: *(giggling)* Don't you think she's changed?

EDO: I think you've changed more, Kyrie. You're almost acting human.

MILA: *(also giggling)* So am I.

EDO: What do you mean by that?

MILA: Nothing.

ZACK: Sounds like the girls have a secret.

KYRIE: No, we don't.

MILA: And even if we did, we wouldn't tell you. Blood sisters never tell.

KYRIE: No way. Not ever.

EDO: Come on, Zack, let's go finish our homework. We'll leave the blood sisters to their silly secrets.

(Zack and Edo leave. As soon as they go, Kyrie and Mila burst out laughing. Lights out.)

ACT TWO, SCENE 2

The biolab. Later that day. Zack and Edo are working at the experiment station.

EDO: I can't get over how much Kyrie has changed. It's like she's completely forgotten that Mila's a Lunarian.

ZACK: She's funny. I think growing up a genius isn't always easy. She's always wanted a best friend. I guess she just needed to get to know Mila a little.

EDO: What's Kyrie experimenting with, anyway?

ZACK: Something to do with bioengineering. That's her specialty.

EDO: Look, here are her experiment notes.

ZACK: How'd you get into that file?

EDO: Computer codes are *my* specialty.

ZACK: You shouldn't be reading that.

EDO: Oh, I doubt that I'll understand it, anyway.

ZACK: Still, those notes are private, right?

EDO: *(reading the computer screen)* Zack, look at this— Mila's name is all through these notes. Something about her DNA. *(He reads a little more.)* It looks like they've conducted some sort of experiment on Mila.

(Kyrie walks in, unnoticed.)

ZACK: Kyrie wouldn't do that.

KYRIE: I wouldn't do what?

EDO: *(angry)* What have you done to Mila?

KYRIE: *(looking at the computer screen)* How did you get into that file?

EDO: Mila! Mila!

ZACK: Kyrie, what's the matter?

KYRIE: It's our secret.

(Mila comes in. Edo runs up to her.)

EDO: Mila, what's this all about?

MILA: What?

EDO: This experiment.

MILA: You weren't supposed to find out.

ZACK: Find out what?

MILA: Kyrie's making me human. I'm going to be human.

EDO: *(astonished)* What?!

MILA: She spliced a little tiny bit of human DNA into my genes so that it will replace my Lunarian DNA. I'm turning human, bit by bit. Look at my hair.

ZACK: *(horrified)* Kyrie, how could you?

KYRIE: Mila, that was our secret.

MILA: I don't care if they know. Besides, you said I could change back any time I want to.

KYRIE: But I like you too much as a human!

MILA: Kyrie, I like it too, so far, but isn't it for me to decide?

KYRIE: *(to Edo)* You've ruined everything. *(Kyrie runs out of the room.)*

MILA: *(to Edo)* She's my friend. Look what you've done! *(She runs out after Kyrie.)*

EDO: What I've done? Seems to me that your sister's the one who's made a mess of everything.

ZACK: I can't believe she would do anything like that.

EDO: She's worse than Dr. Frankenstein. Trying to change my sister into her own image.

ZACK: It's awful. Edo, I'm really upset about this. I'll see to it that Kyrie acts more responsibly.

EDO: On the other hand, maybe it'll be fun to have a human sister.

ZACK: What are you saying?

EDO: Humans can be pretty funny.

ZACK: You're being awfully calm about this.

EDO: It's no big deal.

ZACK: No big deal that my sister has conducted some horrible experiment on Mila?

EDO: Let me show you something. Here, look at this screen. It's part of the computer's hidden code. Read this part.

ZACK: *(reading from the screen)* "All medical techniques are locked in simulation mode." Does that mean what I think . . .

EDO: It means that all of the equipment in this lab is pre-programmed. It acknowledges commands but doesn't execute them. It carries on basic operations without outside control. Kyrie might *think* she spliced Mila's genes, but she didn't really. The computer just made it look like she did. Like the training pods back home.

ZACK: Then why is Mila turning human?

EDO: She's not. They're just both convinced that she is.

ZACK: Well, I still think it's awful.

EDO: Not as awful as what I'm going to do now.

ZACK: What?

EDO: Let's spy on them. Here—this activates the camera in Kyrie's room.

ZACK: You can't do that.

EDO: After what your sister did? Or thinks she did?

ZACK: What do you think they'll do?

EDO: Watch and see. Watch and see.

(Lights out.)

ACT TWO, SCENE 3

Kyrie's room. A few minutes later. Kyrie's room is a mirror image of Mila's room. The same furniture, but in opposite places. Kyrie is face down on her bed, crying. Mila sits at the foot of the bed.

KYRIE: I can't believe they found out.

MILA: My brother'd make a good computer spy.

KYRIE: He'd make a good corpse.

MILA: Don't say that.

KYRIE: I'm sorry. I just didn't want them to find out yet. We were such good friends.

MILA: Aren't we still?

KYRIE: I guess we are.

MILA: You *guess* we are? Come on, we know everything about each other. You told me all about growing up on Earth. I told you everything about the Lunar colonies. I'd say we're the best friends two people can be.

KYRIE: Mila, I'm sorry I was so rotten to you at first.

MILA: You sure were. But I guess I have to forgive my best friend, right?

KYRIE: Are you sorry you're turning human?

MILA: Why?

KYRIE: Well, it's just that I'm starting to think it doesn't matter so much whether you're Lunarian or human.

MILA: Well, I'll be more like you when I'm human.

KYRIE: I know, but you really don't have to be. You're my best friend already. How could we be any closer?

MILA: Well, it'll be fun to find out what color my eyes will be, anyway. *(looking in a mirror)* Look, I think they're going to be blue, like yours.

KYRIE: Mila, let's change you back. Let's put your old DNA back, OK?

MILA: Are you sure you'll still like me?

KYRIE: Of course I will.

MILA: Then let's do it right now! I'll have to give more thought to changing species!

(Lights out.)

ACT TWO, SCENE 4

The biolab. A few minutes later. Zack and Edo are watching the video monitor. They switch it off just as Mila and Kyrie come running in.

MILA: What are you guys still doing in here?

ZACK: Us?

EDO: Just doing some studying.

KYRIE: We've got something to tell you.

MILA: *(pulling Kyrie aside)* No, let's not tell.

ZACK: Yeah, we already—

EDO: *(stepping on Zack's foot)* Shhh! *(He winks at Zack.)*

KYRIE: Oh. Never mind.

ZACK: Yeah, OK. Hey, let's all play a game of antigravity tag in the sky gym.

KYRIE: Sounds great, but you two—

EDO: We'll go on ahead. Join us when you're ready.

(Zack and Edo leave.)

KYRIE: Come on.

MILA: You sure about this?

KYRIE: Yes. You should be you, and I should be me.

MILA: We'll never know what color my eyes would be.

KYRIE: Well, we'll never know what metal color my hair would look like if I were Lunarian, right?

MILA: We won't be blood sisters anymore.

KYRIE: We'll be something better.

MILA: Right.

KYRIE: Come on. Let's get this over with so we can go beat Zack and Edo at antigravity tag.

MILA: OK. Change me back.

KYRIE: Sure thing.

MILA: We'll be different again.

KYRIE: Only a little.

MILA: Yeah, and even closer together. Let's go.

(Mila and Kyrie begin the experiment. Lights out.)

READING FOR UNDERSTANDING

Overview

1. The play takes place on a satellite colony that orbits **(a)** the sun **(b)** the moon **(c)** Earth.

2. Zack and Kyrie are humans from Earth, while Mila and Edo are **(a)** Lunarians **(b)** Martians **(c)** aliens.

Act One

3. Orbiting satellite colonies will grow rapidly because of **(a)** population growth on Earth **(b)** diseases on Earth **(c)** advances in transportation.

4. Kyrie is talented in **(a)** medicine **(b)** chemistry **(c)** bioengineering.

5. When Kyrie first meets Mila and Edo, she treats them **(a)** warmly **(b)** with humor **(c)** rudely.

6. Mila pushes the wrong buttons and **(a)** turns off the heating units **(b)** overloads the computer **(c)** launches the pod.

Act Two

7. Zack urges Kyrie to **(a)** study **(b)** sleep **(c)** give the Lunarians a chance.

8. Kyrie persuades Mila to take part in **(a)** a DNA experiment **(b)** a flight simulation **(c)** a Mars landing.

9. Mila says that the girls would not tell the boys a secret because she and Kyrie are **(a)** too frightened **(b)** sworn to secrecy **(c)** blood sisters.

10. Edo reveals that the girls' experiment does not take place because **(a)** something was wrong with the gene injection **(b)** Mila's body rejected Kyrie's DNA **(c)** the lab equipment was pre-programmed to simulation mode.

11. The four young people go to the sky gym to play
(a) basketball **(b)** computer handball **(c)** anti-gravity tag.
12. We can assume that Mila and Kyrie will
(a) continue to be friends **(b)** part company
(c) resign from the program.

RESPONDING TO THE PLAY

1. Early on Kyrie says, "I want a friend that's like me." How important is it for friends to have lots in common? Are there times when you want a friend who's not like you? Write a paragraph about what you look for in a friend.
2. Skim recent newspapers and magazines for an article about research in the field of genetics. Read the article, and summarize it in a short report to the class. In your report, tell whether you agree or disagree with this kind of research, and explain why.

REVIEWING VOCABULARY

The following sentences are based on the play. Decide which of the words following the sentences best fits each blank. Write your answers on a separate sheet of paper.
1. The families were going to live on the new colony for one month without experts or the _____.
2. Kyrie _____ a tiny amount of human DNA into Mila's genes.
3. Edo discovered that all medical techniques had been locked into _____ mode.
4. When Edo tapped his fingernails on the desk, they made a _____ clatter.
5. Atmospheric changes created a _____ in the first lunar colonists.

6. Zack told Kyrie that there was more to learn than
_____.

Words: *mutation, simulation, media, metallic, genetic, bioengineering, spliced*

THINKING CRITICALLY

1. Of the four characters in the play—Zack, Kyrie, Mila, and Edo—which one was your favorite? Explain why.

2. Kyrie tried to change Mila into a human. How did you react when you read about Kyrie's experiment on Mila?

3. When Edo reveals that the computer was locked in simulation mode, we learn that Kyrie's experiment never really took place at all. Mila is not really turning human. However, the girls think she is. What does this suggest?

4. Toward the end of the play, Kyrie says to Mila, "You should be you, and I should be me." What has Kyrie learned?

5. What does the play suggest about differences that divide people?

WRITING PROJECTS

1. What if something goes wrong when Kyrie tries to put Mila's DNA back? Write a sequel to the play in the form of a brief short story that shows the girls' reactions.

2. Would you like being on a month-long voyage in the Youth Pod? Write a diary entry showing why or why not.

Event Unexplained

Diane Zahler

Do human beings need the thrill of discovery, whatever the dangers may be? This play assumes that we do.

Event Unexplained *takes place in the 21st century. By then, many aspects of space travel have become routine. Most of the action in this play takes place on a space shuttle. To its crew members, this space shuttle has become an old, familiar vehicle. Yet something happens aboard the shuttle that is far from routine.*

Read on to find out how Major N'Deesha Ibo, the play's main character, reacts when she is suddenly thrust into danger.

VOCABULARY WORDS

console (KOHN-sohl) instrument panel
❖ The mission commander was seated at the space-craft's computer *console*.

malfunction (mal-FUNK-shuhn) failure
❖ Any computer *malfunction* may cause the mission to be canceled.

debris (duh-BREE) rubbish; litter
❖ Their team keeps the airport's runways free of *debris* of any kind.

tether (TEHTH-uhr) connecting rope or chain
❖ An astronaut's *tether* connects him or her to the spacecraft during a spacewalk.

pulsate (PUL-sayt) to throb or vibrate
❖ New supernovas *pulsate* with light and energy.

debriefing (dee-BREEF-ing) session in which a person reports information about a job that has just been completed
❖ The astronauts underwent a lengthy *debriefing* when they returned.

transmitted (tranz-MIHT-uhd) sent
❖ I *transmitted* my request by fax to the company.

KEY WORDS

port (POHRT) as one faces forward, the left-hand side of a ship, airplane, or spacecraft
❖ Our cabin was on the *port* side, which was bright and sunny every morning.

Hamlet (HAM-lit) the hero of Shakespeare's tragedy of the same name
❖ The actor who played *Hamlet* in that film was Mel Gibson.

CHARACTERS

N'Deesha Ibo, *a major in the Worldwide Interspace Organization (WIO)*

Annie McSorley, *a major in WIO*

Edvard Czerny, *a lieutenant colonel in WIO*

Zoe Green, *a communications officer*

General Li, *a general in WIO*

Tommy Cohn, *a communications officer*

Colony communications officer

Colonel Proski

Mr. Ibo, *N'Deesha's father*

Mrs. Ibo, *N'Deesha's mother*

Joe Suarez, *N'Deesha's fiancé*

SETTING

Act One

The control room of the space shuttle *Pequod*

Act Two

The Command room at WIO Communications

Act Three

The Command room at WIO Communications

Act Four

The control room of the space shuttle *Pequod*

ACT ONE

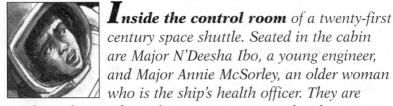 ***Inside the control room*** *of a twenty-first century space shuttle. Seated in the cabin are Major N'Deesha Ibo, a young engineer, and Major Annie McSorley, an older woman who is the ship's health officer. They are dressed in uniforms but not spacesuits. Shuttle air is*

breathable. N'Deesha sits at a complex console. Annie is sitting nearby, drinking coffee.

ANNIE: I'm glad I'm not one of those space colony construction workers. What a life!

N'DEESHA: I know. They can't breathe without tanks, they live for weeks in zero gravity, and they work way too hard.

ANNIE: On the other hand, it'll be great when we can dock at the colony and actually get out of the ship. It's pretty tight in here.

N'DEESHA: That's years down the line. We'll be carrying them food and materials for another decade. Back and forth, back and forth. You know, I thought shuttle work would be a little more exciting. We're just delivery people, really.

ANNIE: Oh, I've been on some trips that you'd have found *too* exciting. Remember when the *Argo* blew a hatch back in '64?

N'DEESHA: You were on that ship? When Lieutenant Duncan was killed?

ANNIE: It happened so fast that there wasn't anything we could do for him. I thought I'd never fly again after that, but you get it in your blood. Once a spacer, always a spacer, they say.

N'DEESHA: I can't imagine doing anything else.

ANNIE: Don't forget, though: we're alone out here. You can feel pretty safe inside one of these shuttles, but the universe is always just outside.

N'DEESHA: *(laughing)* What a comforting thought. *(She stares at the console.)* Hey, what's this? *(She hits a* *button on the console. An automated voice responds.)*

VOICE: Malfunction in Orbiting Maneuvering System engine two.

N'DEESHA: Uh-oh. Lieutenant! Where is he? *(speaking into console)* Lieutenant Czerny!

(Lieutenant Edvard Czerny enters.)

EDVARD: What is it?

N'DEESHA: One of the OMS engines is malfunctioning. We can't slow down enough to land without it.

(Edvard moves to the console, sits, and flips a switch.)

EDVARD: *Pequod* to Command. Come in, Command.

VOICE OF ZOE: Command here. Over.

EDVARD: We have a OMS engine malfunction light. Can you confirm? Over.

(pause)

VOICE OF ZOE: Our sensors indicate your sealer ring is loose. Repair is necessary. Over.

EDVARD: Copy. Over and out. *(turning to N'Deesha)* We have a problem.

N'DEESHA: I'm trained in OMS repair, sir. There's no problem.

EDVARD: Yes, there is, Major. The spacewalk booster pack wasn't cleared by Safety for this flight.

N'DEESHA: *(shrugging)* Well, it's been cleared this year, hasn't it? I'm sure it's all right. Besides, we don't have a choice. If the engine doesn't fire properly, we'll never make re-entry. I'm willing to take the risk.

EDVARD: Have you ever spacewalked before? *(N'Deesha shakes her head.)* The training is excellent, but a little real experience helps. I don't know . . . I should go myself . . . but I'm no engineer. I couldn't do the work. I'll have to clear it with Command. (speaking into console) *Pequod* to Command. Come in.

VOICE OF ZOE: Command here. Over.

EDVARD: Major Ibo has volunteered to repair the engine. The spacewalk booster pack is not okayed. Repeat, the booster pack is not okayed. Over.

(pause)

VOICE OF ZOE: Pack was okayed a sixmonth ago. Safety says it should be fine. Over.

EDVARD: Copy. The ring has to be tightened. The major is going ahead. Over.

VOICE OF ZOE: Information recorded and approved. Over and out.

EDVARD: *(swiveling to face N'Deesha)* Major, don't take any chances. Just walk over, do the job, and return. I don't want a repeat of your training session.

N'DEESHA: *(hiding a grin)* I wouldn't dream of it, Lieutenant.

ANNIE: You know she's wanted to spacewalk ever since she got clearance, sir.

EDVARD: Well, it's a lot different doing it outside than doing it in the zero-grav room. If you dance the Morph in space, you're likely to end up in your own personal, permanent orbit.

ANNIE: *(turning to N'Deesha)* That was you? You were

the student who got caught dancing in zero-grav?
(She laughs.) How long were you on probation?

N'DEESHA: *(with dignity)* That was more than a twelve-month ago. I know better than to fool with *real* zero-grav. *(She walks over to a closet and pulls out a streamlined spacesuit.)* Wow! This thing is ancient. It looks like a fifties model!

ANNIE: Well, this ship isn't usually used for spacewalks anymore. We're a transport shuttle. They probably haven't put in new equipment for years.

N'DEESHA: *(fingering the suit)* As long as there aren't any holes in it, right? *(She holds up a small backpack with two tubes attached.)* I hope these boosters work better than they look.

EDVARD: *(smiling)* Don't worry; there hasn't been an accident in decades. But hey, let's be *careful* out there.

ACT TWO

The Command room at WIO Communications. It is crowded with several large computerized consoles, desks, and radio and telephone equipment. Workers come and go, giving an impression of great busy importance. At one desk sits Zoe Green. She is communicating with N'Deesha through a complicated-looking machine and watching her actions on a radar screen.

ZOE: You're almost done, Major. How are you doing? Any dizziness?

VOICE OF N'DEESHA: Nope. It feels . . . great. Not at all like training. I can't tell what's up or down. It's wild!

ZOE: Don't spin. You'll get sick, and getting sick in a spacesuit is no fun. Okay, our sensors show the ring is sealed.

VOICE OF N'DEESHA: I've got to get the casing back on. These lugs are tight. It's really hard—I can't put any weight on them. I don't have any weight! I'm glad I've been working out. There's one. And the other.

ZOE: *(alarmed)* Major, I'm sighting something on radar scan. It looks like space debris. Do you see anything?

VOICE OF N'DEESHA: No, I—wait. There *is* something. It's between me and the shuttle. Looks like garbage. I thought we cleaned all that up!

ZOE: Fire your boosters, Major. Get out of the way! That garbage could be deadly!

VOICE OF N'DEESHA: *(panicky)* The left booster isn't firing. I'm spinning in circles. The debris—Oh no!

ZOE: Major! *(spins in her chair)* Tommy, she's loose! The tether's been sliced!

(Several other communications officers rush over.)

ZOE: *(to Tommy)* Tommy, get General Li. *(to N'Deesha)* Major, can you hear me? Are you all right?

VOICE OF N'DEESHA: I'm floating away from the ship! What do I do? The left booster won't fire!

ZOE: Stay calm. We'll get you back inside. How much air do you have?

VOICE OF N'DEESHA: I don't know. I can't breathe. I can't breathe!

ZOE: *(sharply)* Calm down, Major! Check your monitor. What does it say?

VOICE OF N'DEESHA: It says . . . 94 minutes. An hour and a half. That's not long. What do I do?

(General Li enters and stands behind Zoe.)

GENERAL LI: Enjoy the view, Major. We're going to contact the Colony. They have a cruiser that they can launch to intercept you. Just relax. *(to Zoe)* Call the Colony. Get me Proski.

ZOE: Hold on, Major. We'll be with you in a minute. *(He presses a switch.)* Command to Colony One. Come in.

(pause)

VOICE OF COLONIST: Colony One receiving. Over.

ZOE: General Li to Colonel Proski. Over.

VOICE OF COLONEL PROSKI: Proski here. Over.

GENERAL LI: Proski, we have a shuttle officer loose. Can you launch your cruiser to intercept her? Over.

VOICE OF COLONEL PROSKI: Sorry, General; impossible. Not enough fuel. That's in our supply request for the next shuttle delivery. Over.

GENERAL LI: Copy. Any ideas?

VOICE OF COLONEL PROSKI: Not a one, sir. Sorry. Over.

(General Li walks away, visibly distressed.)

ZOE: Over and out. General? Can't they get her from the shuttle?

GENERAL LI: *(turning)* They couldn't get close enough. Those shuttles aren't made for delicate work. Either the engines would fry her, or she'd get sucked into the boosters.

ZOE: Then what can we do?

GENERAL LI: She's going to die out there.

ZOE: There's nothing we can do? *(General Li shakes his head.)* General, there must be something. What do I tell her?

GENERAL LI: *(heavily)* I'll tell her. Bring her up, then contact her family. They live nearby, right?

ZOE: I believe so. Her father works in the CompuRoom. *(She turns back to the console.)* Command to Major Ibo. Come in.

VOICE OF N'DEESHA: *(shakily)* Ibo here. How long till the cruiser comes?*(Zoe leaves the room. General Li takes her seat.)*

GENERAL LI: Major, this is General Li. We've talked to Colony One; the cruiser can't come. They have no fuel. We've sent for your family. I'm very sorry, Major.

VOICE OF N'DEESHA: *(rising angrily)* What do you mean? It sounds like you're just giving up! You can't leave me outside! I only have eighty minutes more air!

GENERAL LI: Major, keep in control. We will continue to look for a solution. However, your situation is grave.

VOICE OF N'DEESHA: *(more quietly)* I'm going to die out here. In the middle of all this . . . nothing. *(in a tone of false cheer)* I'll orbit Earth forever, won't I? Just satellites, some space debris, and me. I hope I don't interfere with Earth teleview reception. I'd hate to cause static in teleview land. *(a slightly hysterical giggle)*

(Zoe returns. General Li gives her back her seat.)

ZOE: Is she on? *(General Li nods.)* Major? Your parents are on their way. They'll be here shortly. How are you doing?

VOICE OF N'DEESHA: Oh, fine. Just great. Seventy-five minutes of air and counting—make that 74 minutes. Hey, what's your name, anyway?

ZOE: Communications Officer Green. Zoe Green.

VOICE OF N'DEESHA: You don't mind if I call you Zoe, do you? We don't have too much time to get to know each other, after all. Do you believe in heaven, Zoe? I wish I did. I'm so close to it, anyway. I'd get there in no time.

ZOE: Major—

VOICE OF N'DEESHA: You know, just a little while ago, I was wishing for some excitement. I sure got my wish, didn't I? Only . . . excitement should be loud, don't you think? It's so quiet out here.

ZOE: *(voice trembling)* I'm sorry, N'Deesha. I'm sorry.

VOICE OF N'DEESHA: Don't stop talking, Zoe. I need to hear the sound of a human voice.

ACT THREE

Inside the Command Room. Mr. and Mrs. Ibo, followed by Joe Suarez and General Li, enter. The Ibos and Joe look fearful.

GENERAL LI: Officer Green, find seats for the family. Are we still in contact with the Major?

ZOE: *(She stands.)* Yes, Sir. Do they know—? *(She gestures to the Ibos.)*

GENERAL LI: They know.

(Zoe brings three chairs over to her console.)

ZOE: Ma'am, Sir, you can talk normally and she'll hear you, as long as you don't turn away.

MRS. IBO: *(in a trembling voice)* N'Deesha? Are you there, honey?

VOICE OF N'DEESHA: Mother? Is that you?

MR. IBO: I'm here too, Dee. They tell us you're—you're in trouble.

VOICE OF N'DEESHA: *(She laughs, almost normally.)* Trouble? Is that how they put it? I'm in trouble because some know-nothing okayed this ancient spacesuit! And I couldn't wait to get in it!

(Mrs. Ibo gasps.)

JOE: Dee. Hey, Dee.

VOICE OF N'DEESHA: Oh, Joe—you too?

JOE: *(passionately)* I wish I was out there with you. *Instead* of you.

VOICE OF N'DEESHA: Joe, come on. You're afraid of heights! *(Joe forces a smile.)* This is so weird. I can't believe I'm going to have to say goodbye to you all. I wish I could see you.

JOE: How much . . . how much time—

VOICE OF N'DEESHA: *(matter of factly)* I have about fifteen minutes more air.

JOE: Oh, Dee. I told you not to go into this program. You knew it would be dangerous!

VOICE OF N'DEESHA: Joe, let's not get into that again. You know I've loved it. I'm a spacer—it's in my blood.

JOE: Not down here, with me? With us?

VOICE OF N'DEESHA: I love you. And you too, Mom, Dad. But this . . . space . . . it's me. It's who I am. If I have to die, I'd rather do it up here—or is it down? Anyway, if I have to die, I prefer to spend eternity floating around the galaxy.

MR. IBO: She's right, Joe. This is what she always wanted, since she was a little girl. If she were earth-bound, it would be more than gravity weighing her down.

VOICE OF N'DEESHA: I'm glad you understand, Dad.

MRS. IBO: Dee, darling, I—

VOICE OF N'DEESHA: Whoa. What's that?

ZOE: *(comes to the console)* What's what?

VOICE OF N'DEESHA: I don't know. A glow or something. Is it the cruiser?

ZOE: The cruiser is at the Colony. There's nothing showing on the radar scan.

VOICE OF N'DEESHA: It's coming closer. It's like—is it a spacecraft? Who's up?

ZOE: No one but the *Pequod*.

VOICE OF N'DEESHA: No, that's impossible. There's a craft here.

69

ZOE: General Li! Quickly!

(General Li strides over.)

VOICE OF N'DEESHA: I can't really make out its shape. It seems to sort of . . . pulsate. The lights are getting really close. I can't look straight at it. It makes me dizzy.

GENERAL LI: The radar scan is blank.

(The Ibos stand and clasp each other.)

MR. IBO: Her mind . . . she must be almost out of air.

MRS. IBO: Oh, Dee!

VOICE OF N'DEESHA: *(calmly)* It's the oddest thing. There's this pressure . . . almost like a wind is blowing me. There's no wind in space. What's going on?

GENERAL LI: Look at the scan. She's moving.

ZOE: It's not possible.

VOICE OF N'DEESHA: I can see the shuttle getting closer. Is it coming toward me?

ZOE: The shuttle isn't moving, Major. You are.

GENERAL LI: Raise the shuttle. Have Czerny ready at the hatch.

MRS. IBO: What's going on? I don't understand. Is she all right?

VOICE OF N'DEESHA: Wow. I can see the port hatch. Do you think—*(a crackle of static)*

ZOE: The voice link is gone. Major Ibo? Come in, Major Ibo. No, it's gone. *(She turns to the Ibos helplessly.)*

ACT FOUR

Inside the shuttle control room. Mr. and Mrs. Ibo and Joe have been restricted to another part of the shuttle during N'Deesha's debriefing. Edvard is at the console. Annie is examining N'Deesha with medical instruments. N'Deesha is lying back in a reclining chair.

ANNIE: Blood pressure normal. Heart rate normal. Blood count is fine. My dear, you seem to have come through with no ill effects. Amazing.

N'DEESHA: *(dreamily) Amazing* hardly describes it.

EDVARD: What exactly did it look like?

N'DEESHA: Well . . . it's hard to describe. I didn't notice it till it was almost on top of me. It was like it just appeared, you know? I saw lights, pulsing lights. They were colored, but the colors—well, they weren't any colors I know.

ANNIE: What do you mean?

N'DEESHA: *(sitting up impatiently)* I don't *know*. I can't explain it. They were just different.

ANNIE: Okay, okay. Calm down. Sit back. Tell us what happened next.

N'DEESHA: It all just sounds crazy. The lights were all around me, and suddenly I stopped being afraid. I just felt . . . safe. I knew I wasn't going to die. Then there was a strange feeling . . . like a pressure, as if something was pushing me, and I guess it was. I didn't really feel like I was moving, but I could see the shuttle getting closer and closer. It was as if the ship, or whatever it was, was pushing me toward the *Pequod.*

EDVARD: *(unbelievingly)* Pushing you?

N'DEESHA: *(defensively)* I said it sounded crazy. All I can tell you is how it seemed to me.

ANNIE: The fact is, Lieutenant, she did get back. How else could she have done it?

N'DEESHA: But how should I put it in my report? WIO Command is waiting for it.

ANNIE: *(laughs)* Yes, you're their star. I hear the tele-view reporters are thick as flies down there. You can probably sell your life story for millions.

EDVARD: Just report what happened, Major. Explain what you saw and what you did. Don't draw any conclusions.

N'DEESHA: I don't *have* any conclusions. I'll prepare the report now, sir. *(She exits.)*

EDVARD: Major McSorley, you've had psych training. Couldn't the mind create conditions that would allow her to get back?

ANNIE: *(smiling)* She's too realistic for that.

EDVARD: *(He stands and paces in the cramped room.)* Then you're saying you believe it was a—an alien force?

ANNIE: *(shrugging)* I don't have any other ideas. Do you?

EDVARD: No. But I thought our department's official position was that there is no other life in the universe. There's never been any proof—that we know of.

ANNIE: *(softly)* Maybe they were wrong. After all,

people once believed the Earth was flat. Remember? Scientific theories are being proved and disproved every day. And if it wasn't aliens, what do *you* think happened to her outside?

EDVARD: Look, I'm a military man. If I'm told there is no life in outer space, I believe it. What happened, happened. I accept it. That's all.

ANNIE: Well, as Hamlet said, "There are more things in heaven and earth, Horatio, than are dreamt of in your philosophy."

(They laugh, uncomfortably.)

VOICE OF ZOE: Command to *Pequod*. Come in.

EDVARD: *(returning to the console) Pequod* here. Over.

VOICE OF ZOE: General Li is waiting for Major Ibo's report. Is it ready? Over.

EDVARD: *(to Annie)* See if the Major is ready. *(to Zoe)* Stand by, Command. *(Annie exits.)*

VOICE OF ZOE: Command wishes to inform Major Ibo that her report will be transmitted on teleview.

(Enter N'Deesha and Annie. N'Deesha sits at console.)

N'DEESHA: Major Ibo here. Ready to report. Over.

VOICE OF ZOE: Transmitting.

N'DEESHA: Major N'Deesha Ibo reporting. At fifteen-fifty Western Hemisphere time on Fourmonth thirtieth, twentyseventy-four, I began a spacewalk to repair an OMS engine seal on the shuttle *Pequod*. The left booster on my booster pack misfired, and the tether was cut by space debris. I broke loose in space. Command found that a rescue was not possible. With less than fifteen minutes of air remaining, I faced certain death. However, a spaceshiplike shape appeared near me, and I was aided back to the *Pequod* by the ship or whatever guided it. I reached safety and have been declared fit for service by the health officer.

VOICE OF ZOE: Status of incident?

EDVARD: Incident accidental.

VOICE OF ZOE: Status of officer involved?

ANNIE: Officer in good health, both mentally and physically.

VOICE OF ZOE: *(hesitant)* Status of rescue event?

(pause)

EDVARD: *(turning to N'Deesha)* Major Ibo?

N'DEESHA: Event . . . event unexplained.

VOICE OF ZOE: Repeat, Major?

N'DEESHA: *(more strongly)* Event unexplained.

VOICE OF ZOE: Thank you, Major. See you on Earth. Over and out.

READING FOR UNDERSTANDING

Overview
   1. When and where does the action of the play take place?

Act One
   2. Who is N'Deesha Ibo? For what job does she volunteer?
   3. How has what happened on the *Argo* changed Annie's attitude toward flying now?
   4. What are the two reasons that Edvard is reluctant to let N'Deesha take the spacewalk to repair the sealer ring?

Act Two
   5. How does General Li first propose to save N'Deesha? Why won't his plan work?
   6. How does the debris in space cause a crisis for N'Deesha?
   7. At the end of this act, why does N'Deesha tell Zoe to keep talking?

Act Three
   8. When N'Deesha thinks she is about to die, how does she react to her fate?
   9. What does N'Deesha's father mean when he says that if N'Deesha were earthbound, there would be more than gravity weighing her down?

Act Four
   10. What did the strange spacecraft look like? How does it help N'Deesha?
   11. How do the characters try to explain what

happened to N'Deesha? What are some of the possibilities they discuss?

RESPONDING TO THE PLAY

1. Do you think N'Deesha would make a good friend? Could you rely on her in a tight spot? Write a paragraph telling how you react to her personality. Include evidence from the play to support your response.

2. Edvard says that the astronauts' official position is that there is no other life in the universe. What do you think? Write a paragraph in which you give and explain your opinion.

REVIEWING VOCABULARY

Match each word on the left with the correct definition on the right.

1. debriefing	**a.** sent
2. pulsate	**b.** rubbish
3. debris	**c.** information session
4. malfunction	**d.** instrument panel
5. console	**e.** to throb
6. transmitted	**f.** failure

THINKING CRITICALLY

1. Annie says, "Once a spacer, always a spacer." Mr. Ibo says about N'Deesha that "if she were earthbound, it would be more than gravity weighing her down." What makes Annie and N'Deesha so determined to be astronauts?

2. Why do you think N'Deesha takes the risk of volunteering for a dangerous mission?

3. How did you react to General Li's handling of the situation? Is there anything else he could have done, given the circumstances?

4. Who or what do you think saved N'Deesha?

5. Do you believe that every event has a logical explanation? Or do some things happen that remain unexplained? Give some examples to support your opinion.

WRITING PROJECTS

1. Assume that you are N'Deesha. Using information and hints provided by the dialogue in Acts III and IV, write a diary entry expressing your feelings about the remarkable rescue and your return to the *Pequod*. Date your entry one week after the events took place.

2. Many popular movies and television series deal with space exploration. Select one of your favorite episodes from these dramas, and write a summary of the action. Share your summary with a small group of classmates.

The Seven Sisters

Chuck Haines

Research in genetics has opened up a world of new possibilities. But as yet no one has achieved the genetic miracles you will read about in this play.

Our story opens at a research station in the frozen land of Antarctica. Scientists have found a body in the ice. It has lain frozen there for about ten thousand years. They hope that the body will reveal something about human life ten thousand years ago. They also want to use the body to perform a ground-breaking experiment in genetics.

The experiment ends in a way that none of the scientists could have expected. It points to a secret of long ago—something that reaches beyond science into the shadowy world of dreams.

VOCABULARY WORDS

fissure (FIHSH-uhr) crack
* ❖ The X-ray shows a *fissure* in his wrist.

intact (ihn-TAKT) whole
* ❖ The other vase was *intact*.

artifacts (AHR-tuh-fakts) things made by human work
* ❖ These *artifacts* were used by the Romans to sculpt marble.

fragmented (FRAG-mehnt-uhd) broken
* ❖ One vase was *fragmented* beyond repair.

contaminated (kuhn-TAM-uh-nait-uhd) polluted
* ❖ Don't drink that water because it's *contaminated*.

cavity (KAV-uh-tee) hollow space
* ❖ The *cavity* was full of gas.

pathology (pa-THAHL-uh-gee) having to do with disease
* ❖ The *pathology* test showed she had flu.

surrogate (SER-uh-gayt) substitute
* ❖ He could not be there, so he sent a *surrogate*.

barren (BEHR-uhn) not producing crops
* ❖ Nothing grows on *barren* soil.

constellation (kahn-stuh-LAY-shuhn) group of stars
* ❖ The *constellation* looked just like a drawing of a lion.

KEY WORDS

DNA a long, chemical molecule in the human body that contains the *gene* (JEEN) that controls a person's inherited traits.
* ❖ The *DNA* molecule is the blueprint or code of life.

CHARACTERS

Hub Robins, *Director, Biological Research Lab (BRL)*
Earl Martin, *Biologist, U.S. Geological Survey (USGS)*
Pam Slakow, *Biologist, USGS*
Dave Barnhart, *Technician, BRL*
Dr. Barb Joseph, *Molecular Geneticist, BRL*
Susan Lane, *Anthropologist, BRL*
Rex Burch, *Geologist, USGS*
Dr. Willa Hall, *Psychiatrist*
Dr. Shirley Grant, *Behavioral Scientist*
Julie, *product of the world's first chromosome transfer*
Julie's six sisters

SETTING

Act One

A conference room in the Long-Term Ecological
Research Station at Ellsworth, Antarctica, 2004.

Act Two

Scene 1

The Molecular Genetics lab, part of the Biological
Research Laboratory (BRL) organization in Rockville,
Maryland. Two weeks later.

Scene 2

Library. A few minutes later.

Scene 3

Main conference room at BRL. An hour later.

Scene 4

Main conference room at BRL. Fifteen minutes later.

Act Three

Office of Dr. Shirley Grant at BRL. Fourteen years later.

Act Four

Near Santa Teresa, Peru. Seven years later.

ACT ONE

 *A conference room in the* Long-Term *Ecological Research Station at Ellsworth, Antarctica, 2004. A large map of Antarctica hangs on one wall. A detailed map, titled "Long-Term Ecological Research Study Area," hangs on another wall. A third wall holds a satellite map of Antarctica. There are no windows. Hub, Pam, and Earl sit at the conference table, each wearing heavy sweaters. Hub, wearing a stocking cap, is shivering and rubbing his hands.*

HUB: *(He coughs.)* Thanks again, Earl, for inviting me down, but how can you live here in this cold?

EARL: Ha. This is our summer. You should try the winters. Well, let's get started. Pam is the one who recovered the body. *(He looks over at Pam.)*

PAM: *(She stands and walks to a large map at the front of the room.)* I'd like to summarize what has occurred to date. On February second, Kyle Waska of the USGS was setting up a geological data collection site in a valley of the Pensacola Mountains. That's about four hundred and fifty miles south of here.

HUB: Was this part of their Long-Term Ecological Research project?

PAM: Yes, Hub. The Pensacola Mountains are at the southern edge of the study area. Kyle had been in the area for several days when the earthquake occurred. He spotted a new ice fissure in the side of valley. That's where he found her body. Kyle contacted his supervisors back at Ellsworth. They then informed the Biological Research Team. Hank and I were sent by helicopter to the area to bring her back here for examination.

HUB: Were there any problems in removing the body?

PAM: The earthquake made a fissure in the ice a half-mile long. The ice wall was about ten feet high, with a very smooth surface. You could see about three or four feet into the ice. Her right shoulder and hip were sticking out. *(She looks toward the ceiling.)*

HUB: How difficult was it to get her out of there?

PAM: The ice next to her body was cracked from earth movement. That made it a lot easier to retrieve her. We took as much of the surrounding ice as we could.

HUB: I've seen your photos. The body looks intact.

PAM: She's in very good shape. She's stayed frozen for about ten thousand years. So far, we've only examined her for superficial wounds. Besides a few scrapes on her knees, she seems uninjured.

HUB: What about the X-rays?

PAM: The X-rays show a normal skeleton and intact internal organs. We estimate that she was between twenty and twenty-five years old. Everything is perfectly preserved, even the food in her stomach.

HUB: What do you think happened?

PAM: She appears to have been very healthy, so I would rule out starvation or illness. She probably froze to death after being caught in a storm.

HUB: How can I help you?

PAM: Your Molecular Biology group can isolate her DNA. Her skin cells still have elasticity. She froze

83

before the cells had time to break down. This is the first time we have had the chance to isolate DNA from a prehistoric human. The other prehistoric bodies that have been found in ice had begun to decay by the time they were frozen. So their DNA was already broken down.

HUB: Tell me about the artifacts you found on her. *(He reaches for a notebook and pen on the desk.)*

PAM: Fiber analysis shows that her ankle-length dress was made of leather. It was trimmed with the fur of a feline—probably an extinct species. She had fur-lined leggings of the same material. Her boots were also leather. She had a strange necklace of small pearls and seven pottery beads shaped like stars. At the center of the necklace was a stone carved in the shape of the Pleiades group of stars.

HUB: *(under his breath)* The Pleiades group of stars? Why that's the seven sisters . . .

PAM: What?

HUB: Nothing . . . go on.

PAM: Each ear was pierced with a small bird bone. She also had a large leather bag hung over her left shoulder. X-rays show a couple of smaller bags containing food grains, a few small wooden tools, and some stone charms.

HUB: Is that about it?

PAM: Yes, Hub. I think so. Her body will be ready for your flight to Rockville in about two hours.

HUB: Thanks a lot, Pam. We'll see what the people in our labs can do.

(The stage goes dark.)

ACT TWO, SCENE 1

The Molecular Genetics lab, part of the Biological Research Laboratory (BRL) organization in Rockville, Maryland. Two weeks later. World famous for developing genetic transfer techniques on plants, scientists at the lab are now experimenting with the transfer of human genes. The lab is filled with advanced scientific instruments, computers, and various test tubes. At one end, Dave is speaking on the telephone at his desk while Barb looks at a cell culture dish.

DAVE: Two days. We need two days to make certain the cells can be used. When? OK. See you then. *(He hangs up.)* Barb, are you up to specimen five eleven yet?

BARB: I'm just now examining it. Come and take a look.

DAVE: *(excited)* Perfect. I didn't think we could do it, but this cell layer is perfect.

BARB: Should I get some more samples or wait until we're ready to transfer the chromosomes to the eggs?

DAVE: Let's wait. I'm glad we followed your intuition.

BARB: Well, I'll see you later in the conference room.

(The stage goes dark.)

ACT TWO, SCENE 2

The main conference room at BRL, an hour later. Hub, Susan, Dave, Rex, and Barb are sitting around the table with notebooks and pens in front of them. A slide projector is at the side. Hub is speaking quietly and looking at his watch.

HUB: I thought we might start with Susan's review of her findings.

SUSAN: Ed, would you turn on the slide projector? We've identified a number of plants and seeds in her bags. There were three plant roots wrapped in woven grass stems. *(Susan nods toward the screen, which shows a slide of the bag and the roots.)* We can't identify the grass. The botanist is still examining the roots. The seeds we found were also in a small leather bag. *(She signals and the projection switches to a new slide.)* All of these seeds can be found in western South America. We also found six small tubers, which you see there next to the roots.

REX: Do you think the tubers are one of the classical South American potato species?

SUSAN: Yes. We also found some dried fruit, probably from a variety of passionflower, and squash rinds and five types of pollen.

HUB: Is there any possibility that the bags have been contaminated with any present-day pollen?

SUSAN: Very little chance. Pam was very careful to seal the bag at the site where the body was found. I don't think we have to worry about contamination.

HUB: What else did you find?

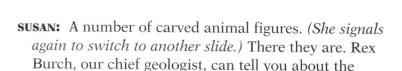

SUSAN: A number of carved animal figures. *(She signals again to switch to another slide.)* There they are. Rex Burch, our chief geologist, can tell you about the stones.

REX: We're certain that they came from the central Andes Mountains. Their mineral composition is unique. I think we can pin down an exact location in less than a week. My best guess is that the stones are from the Cordillera region in Peru. We have people in the field working on it.

HUB: *(He sniffs impatiently.)* Peru! That's at least four thousand miles from our site! Why would she have been so far from home? Where was she going?

SUSAN: *(She shrugs.)* We call her Star because of her star necklace and because one of the stones in her bag also has a star pattern carved on it. *(She sits down.)*

HUB: Do you have a slide of the star pattern?

SUSAN: Yes. *(She signals the projectionist once more.)* You can see that the seven stars in the pattern resemble the constellation Pleiades.

HUB: The Seven Sisters again . . .

SUSAN: What are you referring to?

HUB: That's just what the Greeks called that constellation because—of its many stars—only seven could be seen with the naked eye.

SUSAN: Barb, could you pick it up from here?

BARB: *(Barb stands and signals the projectionist.)* This is a picture of Star in the lab's Cold Room. You can see that she was well nourished. Her hair is jet black and tied behind in a bun. Unlike the ice man found in the Alps in 1992, she had no tattoos.

HUB: Where did you open her body cavity?

BARB: We made a small incision just below the sternum to get the organ analyses.

HUB: Are those tests completed yet?

BARB: All the pathology tests indicate that she was healthy and well-nourished. The only thing unusual was that Star's ovaries were much larger than those of women today.

HUB: Have you found out how old she is now?

SUSAN: We sent bone samples to four different labs. Each lab estimates an age of ten thousand years, plus or minus a hundred and seventy-five years. The plant material was also estimated at the same age.

SUSAN: Barb, have you completed the chromosomal studies?

BARB: We have finally isolated a complete set of chromosomes. Tests show that she was Asian.

(Hub is suddenly lost in reflection, an absent-minded look on his face. The others notice it all at once. There is an awkward silence.)

BARB: *(clearing her throat)* Um . . . Hub . . . Dr. Robins?

HUB: *(hesitantly)* I was just thinking . . .

BARB: *(impatiently)* Yes?

HUB: Wasn't there some South American Indian group who used the same word for the Pleiades star cluster and for *year*?

SUSAN: *(impatient)* Can we get back on track now? What about her hemoglobin genes?

BARB: Closest link with Asian populations as well.

REX: Or Native American.

BARB: *(nearly sarcastic)* Well, of course we all know that contemporary theory sees the first Native Americans as coming from Asia across the Bering Strait.

SUSAN: What is the status on chromosomal transfer?

HUB: *(troubled)* Can we take a half-hour break?

(The stage goes dark.)

ACT TWO, SCENE 3

Hub is in a small library, bent over a thick, ancient-looking book.

HUB: *(reading out loud to himself)* This family of seven visible stars served as the seven guardians of the year. Each had its task in watching over and protecting the people. The stars worked in harmony to preserve this Indian mountain nation—like a family of seven loving sisters.

(He closes the book and puts his hands over his face, lost in thought.)

(The stage goes dark.)

ACT TWO, SCENE 4

The same conference room, fifteen minutes later.

HUB: I think we all realize that what we discuss during the rest of this meeting is to be kept in this room. I'd like to introduce two new visitors. *(He points to the two people.)* This is Dr. Willa Hall, a physician and psychiatrist, and my daughter, Dr. Shirley Grant, a social scientist who is researching some aspects of surrogate parenting. Barb—ready to continue?

BARB: We have isolated cells from Star that have whole chromosomes.

SUSAN: When will you try the chromosomal transfer?

HUB: We are here to decide the best time.

SHIRLEY: Could you please explain more about the transfer?

BARB: During the last year, my lab has been developing a technique to transfer chromosomes in animals. Now we are ready for a human experiment. We're going to put Star's full complement of chromo-somes—that's all twenty-three pairs—in a living woman to create a baby.

SHIRLEY: But how is that possible?

BARB: We have women who will donate their eggs. Using microscopic surgery, we will put a syringe inside the nucleus of the donor's egg. Then we mere-ly extract the donor's set of chromosomes.

SHIRLEY: You can put the syringe directly into the nucleus of Star's egg and remove the chromosomes?

BARB: Yes. That's the easy part. Then we have to use a

second syringe to insert Star's chromosomes into the nucleus of the living woman's egg. If we can do it, we will have a human egg with a complete set of chromosomes.

HUB: How soon can you be ready to go?

BARB: We need two days for the transfer, then three days to achieve the right size for implanting into the surrogate mother.

WILLA: How many women are you planning to implant with this woman's chromosomes?

HUB: *(suddenly blurting out a suggestion)* Why don't we try seven?

BARB: Good idea. The odds are that one embryo will make it.*(Shirley and Willa speak in rapid succession, their questions overlapping.)*

WILLA: How do you select the surrogate mothers?

SHIRLEY: What kind of follow-up procedures do you plan to track the baby's development?

WILLA: And do your surrogate mothers know that the chromosomes in the egg are coming from a 10,000-year-old corpse?

(The stage goes dark.)

ACT THREE, SCENE 1

Fourteen years later. The office of Dr. Shirley Grant at BRL. She is sitting at a desk, reading a report to Dr. Willa Hall.

SHIRLEY: "All seven embryo implants from Star's chromosomes worked. Surrogate mothers were selected on the basis of their families and emotional stability. Each gave birth to a healthy, normal girl."

WILLA: How did the social and emotional development of the girls compare?

SHIRLEY: That's the bizarre part. The seven girls have been raised by separate families. But exactly at age seven, each girl began to have similar strange dreams. *(She looks at Willa.)*

WILLA: *(doubting)* But how significant is that, Shirley? Many children of that age report vivid dreams.

SHIRLEY: Willa, I'm talking about the very same dream!

(Willa is stunned. She and Shirley gaze in silence at each other for a moment.)

WILLA: These girls must be in contact with each other. They're pulling a fast one on us.

SHIRLEY: How could they be? There's no way they could know about each other. Their mothers were sworn to secrecy.

WILLA: Then what's going on?

SHIRLEY: There's more. They also have identical personalities on the MMPI and the skills tests. You would think that living in different environments would cause some difference. Even identical twins raised in separate environments show some differences. These girls are more alike than most identical twins!

WILLA: Do you intend to let them see each other? I don't think we should—not until we discuss a reason for these strange similarities.

SHIRLEY: I've brought the one named Julie in for an interview.

WILLA: Why her?

SHIRLEY: She's been so lost in her dream world that it seems to be all she can talk about. Her mother was getting worried. So she called me and made an appointment.

WILLA: Do you want me to stay for the interview?

SHIRLEY: Why don't you wait in the side office—the conference room. You can listen to our conversation through the microphone.

(Willa leaves. Enter Julie.)

SHIRLEY: Hi, Julie, how are you today?

JULIE: I'm OK, but I wish Mom didn't have to take me out of school again. There's a field trip to the museum today. We're studying Native American life in the Americas.

(Suddenly her eyes are caught by a group of small, carved animal figures—the same shown in the slide during the conference at BRL.)

JULIE: What are those?

SHIRLEY: Well, because you missed the field trip, I'll let you look at these very old rocks just as if you were at the museum. *(Julie looks extremely interested.)* Here. These stones were carved a long time ago. Look at the different colors.

(Julie handles the stones and seems to recognize them immediately. Her eyes glow with excitement.)

JULIE: Where are my sisters? Have they been here?

SHIRLEY: What do you mean, Julie?

JULIE: My sisters. I can see them suddenly—just like in my dreams.

SHIRLEY: Tell me about your sisters, Julie.

JULIE: *(She looks confused.)* Dr. Grant, you already know about my sisters. I dreamed that you knew they would all be born.

SHIRLEY: *(with a deliberately controlled voice)* Those are just dreams, Julie. They are not real.

JULIE: But I've seen them! They are real. My dreams are real.

SHIRLEY: Then where are your sisters now?

JULIE: *(a little upset)* I want to go home, Dr. Grant.

SHIRLEY: Let's talk a little bit more. Then I'll call your mother and have her pick you up.

JULIE: *(urgently)* I don't want to go home with my mother. I want to go to my old home.

SHIRLEY: But you've lived in the same house since the day you were born.

(Julie looks down at the stone figures in her hands.)

JULIE: These belong to me and my six sisters.

SHIRLEY: *(somewhat sternly)* Who told you about your sisters, Julie? How did you know about them? Tell me the truth now!

JULIE: I am telling you the truth! I met them in my dreams!

SHIRLEY: Do you mind if I bring in Dr. Hall so that she

can talk with us, too?

(Julie nods "yes" without enthusiasm.)

SHIRLEY: *(raising her voice slightly)* Come in, Dr. Hall.

(Willa enters, looking astonished.)

WILLA: Please tell us both about your sisters, Julie.

JULIE: They are just like me. They also see me. They also want to go home.

WILLA: What do they look like?

JULIE: Just like me. All of my sisters look like me. But each likes a different part of the year. Each is like a season. One is like the season of planting. The other is the season of the long rains. Then there is my sister who is the tender one, like new green stalks in the fields. Then there is the barren one. We spend a lot of time comforting her. And there is also the one of the long days and short nights when the sun is always shining. Finally, there is my sister of the harvest. I already told you about her.

WILLA: And which sister are you, Julie? You didn't tell us about yourself.

JULIE: *(hesitantly)* I am the protective sister. The keeper of the dream.

SHIRLEY: Where are your sisters now, Julie? And what are they doing?

JULIE: They all dream like me, and we all want to go to our old home.

WILLA: Where is your old home, Julie?

JULIE: The mountains. Our home is in the mountains.

Somebody took us away.

SHIRLEY: Julie, when do you dream about your sisters?

JULIE: I dream about them all the time.

WILLA: Do you remember when you first dreamed about them?

JULIE: I think so. It was a long time ago. I saw them sitting by a fire. It was harvest time. One of them was very happy because the harvest had been good. They were looking at me.

WILLA: And then did you dream about them again?

JULIE: Of course.

WILLA: Was it a happy dream?

(Julie suddenly looks pale and upset.)

JULIE: Oh, no. It wasn't a happy dream. My sisters were weeping, and so was I.

SHIRLEY: Why were you weeping, Julie?

JULIE: Because it was the time of the barren sister. There was no harvest. The soil had given us nothing. We were so horribly worried. The barren sister was weeping. We were afraid because we had nothing to eat.

WILLA: *(gently)* Julie, I think—

JULIE: *(interrupting)* But then there was the last dream, the one I just had.

SHIRLEY: Tell us about it.

JULIE: I don't like to think about it . . . But then we were very hungry. There was almost no food. Many of our people had died. We felt that the seasons no longer watched over us. Our people were angry at us because they thought we had failed them. There was just enough food left to put into my mother's sack so that she would be able to make her journey.

SHIRLEY: Where was she going, Julie?

JULIE: To find new lands. Or at least to find an answer . . .

WILLA: Do you still talk to your sisters in your dreams?

JULIE: We don't talk like you talk. We don't talk to each other like this. I just close my eyes, and I see them. They're like stars twinkling in the sky. It makes me feel good not to say any words. I just know what they think. I wish I could make you understand.

WILLA: Do your sisters want to tell us anything?

JULIE: We feel that it's time for us to go home. My sisters want to go home to the mountains.

WILLA: Do you feel that you are different from other people, Julie?

JULIE: I don't know. My dreams tell of different places. Where do I really come from? Why don't I look anything like my mother?

(Shirley and Willa look uncomfortably at one another.)

WILLA: Tell her.

SHIRLEY: She's not exactly your mother, Julie.

(Instead of looking upset, Julie looks excited.)

JULIE: She isn't?

SHIRLEY: Fourteen years ago, a woman named Star

was found buried in ice near the South Pole. Star had been in the ice for more than ten thousand years.

JULIE: *(Her face brightens.)* I read about Star in school.

WILLA: What did you think about Star, Julie?

JULIE: *(hesitant to admit it)* I've had many dreams about Star.

WILLA: What did your dreams tell you about Star?

(Julie doesn't answer.)

SHIRLEY: *(gently)* Star's eggs were used to make your mother pregnant with you, Julie. Those eggs were also implanted in six other women.

JULIE: *(gasping)* My sisters and I are one with Star!

SHIRLEY: *(reluctant)* In a sense.

JULIE: That's just what they all said. My sisters always talk about Star.

WILLA: They do? What do you mean? What did they tell you?

JULIE: I can't explain everything. My sisters don't use words. We don't talk like this. We . . .

WILLA: We talk to each other without speaking?

JULIE: *(firmly, looking at Willa and Shirley)* I want you to tell me about my real mother, where I come from.

SHIRLEY: I think you already know, Julie, from your dreams.

(Julie closes her eyes tight. It is as if she is no longer in the room. Shirley and Willa gaze at her in silent awe.)

JULIE: So that's why our Mother had to leave our mountains . . . because our people were starving. . . . So that is why she went south, in search of the new lands . . . or at least in search of an answer . . .

SHIRLEY: And then what happened, Julie?

JULIE: She did not fear because she thought her seven daughters would guide her . . . from the heavens. . . . She knew we would always be there watching over her. She kept us near her in the necklace that she wore around her neck.

(Julie bursts into tears. Shirley takes her in her arms.)

JULIE: *(sobbing)* But we failed . . . we failed.

(The stage goes dark.)

ACT FOUR

Seven years later. A mountainside in southern Peru, near a small village called Santa Teresa. The seven sisters are working in the fields, under the shadow of Machu Picchu. If they could be seen from above, they would form a pattern that resembles the Pleiades. Each is wearing a leather, fur-trimmed dress, leather boots, and a necklace with only one star. Each sister collects corn pollen in a leather bag.

JULIE: Bring the pollen to me, my sisters. It is time for the Great Journey.

(They gather together, each one puts pollen into the old leather bag that Julie is holding. It is Star's bag. Each sister speaks as she places her share of pollen in the bag.)

SISTER 1: That the earth may accept our seed.

SISTER 2: That the earth may drink of the long rains.

SISTER 3: That the new green stalks may embrace the sun.

SISTER 4: That the fields may rest barren for a season, waiting for the new planting.

SISTER 5: That the days may be long and the tall stalks reach to the heavens.

SISTER 6: That the harvest may be plentiful.

JULIE: We will return to the place where our mother stopped. Now it is time to cross the frozen ocean to the south. Perhaps we will find what she was looking for. Perhaps we will find the new lands, or at least some kind of answer. We will return to our mother, just like the stars return each night to the darkened sky.

(Slowly, the sky grows orange as the sun sets. Finally, only the star necklace of each sister can be seen. They twinkle in the darkness like a constellation made of seven stars.)

READING FOR UNDERSTANDING

The following paragraph summarizes the play. Decide which of the words below the paragraph best fits in each blank. Write your answers on a separate sheet of paper.

A body frozen in **(1)**_____ was found in the **(2)**_____ Mountains. Aside from scrapes on the knees, it was **(3)**_____. The person probably died because she **(4)**_____ to death during a storm. Around the body's neck was a **(5)**_____ with seven pottery beads shaped like **(6)**_____. After running tests, scientists found that the body was that of an **(7)**_____ woman. They implanted her **(8)**_____ in seven **(9)**_____ mothers. The daughters who were born to these mothers had the same **(10)**_____. They were more **(11)**_____ than **(12)**_____ twins. One of the girls said that she already knew her **(13)**_____. She also wanted to go back to her **(14)**_____ in the **(15)**_____. Long ago, the sisters' people almost **(16)**_____ to death. Their **(17)**_____ went in search of new **(18)**_____. The sisters were **(19)**_____. They decided to continue their mother's **(20)**_____.

Words: *lands, dreams, froze, Asian, stars, identical, reunited, ice, journey, starved, alike, mother, home, mountains, sisters, necklace, uninjured, surrogate, Pensacola, chromosomes*

RESPONDING TO THE PLAY

1. Julie believes more strongly in her dreams than she does in science. Have you ever had dreams that seemed more real than everyday life? Do you feel there are truths that science never can discover?

Write a paragraph that shows your views.

2. The seven sisters believed that they had a mission in life. They felt that they had no choice but to complete their mission. Do you think that people have missions in life? Have you ever felt that you had a mission to complete?

REVIEWING VOCABULARY

Match each word on the left with the correct definition on the right.

1. artifacts	**a.** crack
2. barren	**b.** broken
3. cavity	**c.** substitute
4. constellation	**d.** whole
5. contaminated	**e.** things made by human work
6. fissure	**f.** hollow space
7. fragmented	**g.** not producing crops
8. intact	**h.** polluted
9. surrogate	**i.** group of stars
10. pathology	**j.** having to do with disease

THINKING CRITICALLY

1. What character in the play first has an idea about Star's real identity? What are the clues?
2. What does Julie say to Shirley that makes her believe that Julie is telling the truth? Would you believe her as quickly as Shirley did?
3. How is it possible that the seven sisters are more alike than identical twins?
4. Of the seven sisters, whom do you consider the leader? Why?
5. What did Star look for in Antarctica? How was this journey like one her people might have made centuries ago?

6. Which events in this play could occur in real life? Which could never occur? Explain your answer.

WRITING PROJECTS

1. Imagine that you are Julie and that you are able to write a letter to Star, your mother. Or imagine that you can communicate with her through your thoughts or in dreams. Describe what you think your future actions might be. Then write a two-paragraph letter or a two-paragraph description of your dream.

2. Start with Julie's visit to Shirley's office and write a new ending for this play. Keep all of the same characters and try not to change the setting. If you make these changes, be prepared to explain them. Remember to explain the action through the characters.

Jupiter Park

Jeffrey Cooper

Imagine what the world of the future might be like. In this play, the author imagined that food would be produced by computers. Oranges would no longer come from trees, or eggs from chickens.

But some things never change. Boys and girls still go out on dates. However, in this future world, a boy and girl from two different planets can meet and date in virtual reality. As advanced as this world seems, it still has some old-fashioned views that you will recognize.

Alan RVJ347 and Melanie K44 are a futuristic Romeo and Juliet. Alan comes from Earth, and Melanie from the space colony of Io. Their families disapprove of their dating. But each finally meets the other in a computer-generated theme park. Find out what happens when these two citizens of the universe become acquainted.

VOCABULARY WORDS

interplanetary (in-tuhr-PLAN-uh-tair-ee) between planets
❖ The first *interplanetary* mission may be launched to Mars with astronauts very soon.

downloaded (DOWN-lohd-uhd) transferred from one computer to another
❖ Jim *downloaded* the program onto a disk.

orbit (OHR-biht) to circle around
❖ The moon *orbits* Earth.

virtual reality (VER-choo-wuhl ree-AL-uh-tee) artificial environments created with computer sensors in a helmet and glove to duplicate experience
❖ The pilot learned how to fly the new plane by use of *virtual reality*.

colonize (KAHL-uh-nyz) to settle
❖ No one can *colonize* Antarctica because of its harsh climate.

cylinder (SIHL-uhn-duhr) shape with two equal sides and a curved surface
❖ The corn came in a metal *cylinder*.

hologram (HAHL-uh-gram) three-dimensional photo made with a laser beam
❖ The *hologram* of the President was lifelike.

dioramas (dy-uh-RAHM-uhz) lifelike models
❖ *Dioramas* of animals can be seen in the Museum of Natural History.

CHARACTERS

Alan RVJ347, *age 16*
Edna and William, *his parents*
Lori, *his sister, age 9*
Melanie K44, *age 16*
Alice and Bert, *her parents*
Louis, *age 9, her brother*
Walter, *Alan's friend*
Jemma, *Melanie's friend*

SETTING

Act One
The kitchen of Alan's home on Earth, one morning in the year 2222

Act Two
The kitchen of Melanie's home on the Io colony, the same morning

Act Three
The main gate at Jupiter Park, a Virtual Reality construct

Act Four
The Time Travel Museum at Jupiter Park

ACT ONE

*T**he curtain opens on the futuristic** kitchen of Alan RVJ347 and his family in the year 2222. Alan's mother, Edna, and sister, Lori, are seated at the breakfast table. Mother and daughter both gaze intently at the tiny computer screens that float just above the table and move for the actors' reading convenience. William* *stands before a sliding wall panel with an empty plate in his hand.*

WILLIAM: Does anyone else want more eggs?

EDNA: *(holding out her plate without looking up from her computer screen)* Thanks.

WILLIAM: Lori?

LORI: *(staring at her screen)* What?

WILLIAM: Do you want more eggs?

LORI: *(looking at her father)* What, Dad?

WILLIAM: I asked if you wanted more eggs.

LORI: Oh. *(looking at her plate as if seeing it for the first time)* No, thanks, Dad.

(William presses a button, and a sliding panel opens. He puts the two plates inside, and the panel closes. A chime sounds almost immediately and the sliding door opens. William removes two plates full of scrambled eggs and hands one to his wife.)

(Alan enters.)

WILLIAM: *(offering his plate to Alan)* Have some eggs, Alan.

ALAN: Thanks, Dad. *(He takes the plate and sits down at the table.)*

LORI: According to my teacher, people used to eat eggs that came out of chickens!

WILLIAM: *(ringing for another plate and joining the family at the table)* Is that right? They ate *chicken* eggs?

EDNA: Really, William. I don't think it's necessary to encourage the child.

LORI: But my teacher said—

EDNA: I'm sure that people ate a lot of disgusting things before synth-food was invented. That doesn't mean we have to talk about it at the breakfast table. Let's just be grateful that we live in the 23rd century and that we don't have to eat eggs from birds in the morning!

ALAN: Speaking of great inventions, would it be all right if I plugged into the VR machine tonight?

WILLIAM: Now, Alan. Virtual Reality isn't some kind of toy that you get to take out and play with when you have nothing better to do.

ALAN: Dad! I'm sixteen years old! Walter's parents let him use the VR machine all the time.

WILLIAM: What Walter does or doesn't do in the privacy of his own home is between him and his parents. In this house, we take virtual reality very seriously.

ALAN: I know that, Dad. It's not as if I'm planning to take a joy-ride across the universe or anything crazy.

EDNA: What *are* you planning?

ALAN: As a matter of fact, I have a date tonight.

LORI: A date? You mean . . . like . . . with a girl?

ALAN: *(sarcastically)* No, Lori, with a Martian fire-worm.

EDNA: Anyone we know?

ALAN: Not really, Mom. She doesn't live around here.

WILLIAM: You met someone from out of town?

ALAN: Actually, someone from another planet.

LORI: Uh-oh!

EDNA: Alan! You know how your father and I feel about interplanetary dating! Aren't there enough nice girls right here on Earth? Where did you meet this person, anyway?

ALAN: We haven't actually met, Mom. Walter downloaded this holo-dating program off the SpaceNet, and we figured we'd key in just for fun.

WILLIAM: And now you've got yourself a date with some strange girl from off-planet.

ALAN: She sounds really nice, Dad. She lives on the Io colony—

WILLIAM: The Io colony? Are you telling me this girl lives in one of those giant bubbles that orbit Jupiter?

ALAN: I think they call them *domes*, Dad. Anyway, that's why I want to use the VR machine. There's this new Virtual Reality program called "Jupiter Park." It's like an amusement park, only it has live volcanoes, a Time Travel Museum and a petting zoo—

EDNA: I don't care if it has a three-ring circus. No son of mine is going out with a girl from the Io colony.

ALAN: Why not, Mom? Don't you and Dad always say it's wrong to judge people by the way they look or where they come from?

WILLIAM: We were talking about regular Earth people, Alan. The Io colonists are nothing like us. They're a whole different breed.

LORI: A girl in my class has a cousin on Mars.

EDNA: At least Mars isn't located halfway across the solar system!

ALAN: It's not as if I'm planning to hop a starbus to Io, Mom! It's only a virtual date. I'll be in my room plugged into the VR machine the whole time!

WILLIAM: And what if you and this colonist girl decide you want to see each other again? It takes three whole days to get to Io, and that's if the trip can be scheduled.

ALAN: It's only a first date, Dad. I'm not planning to marry the girl!

EDNA: I should hope not! No one in our family has ever married an off-planet person, much less an Io colonist.

ALAN: *(rising to his feet)* You're not being fair, Mom! You don't even *know* anyone from Io!

EDNA: That's true, Alan. I don't. But I *do* know what they're like. Most of the people who set out two centuries ago to colonize the solar system were the sort of people who couldn't find a place for themselves in respectable society on Earth. Some of them were just misfits.

LORI: My teacher said that some of them were criminals who were sent away because the jails were too crowded.

ALAN: But not all of them! A lot of them were decent, hard-working people who just wanted to make a fresh start for themselves on a new world.

WILLIAM: Nevertheless, Alan, their customs are very different from ours. I've heard stories—

ALAN: *(angrily)* I don't care what kind of stories you've heard!

EDNA: Alan!

ALAN: *(sitting)* I'm sorry, Dad. I just don't see what harm it could possibly do if I go out on this date. At least I'd find out for myself if the things they say about off-planet people are true.

EDNA: And what if you and this colonist girl have nothing in common?

ALAN: Her name is Melanie, Mom, and we have plenty in common. The holo-program said we were a perfect match. Besides, if anything goes wrong, I can always unplug.

EDNA: I'll tell you what, Alan. You can go on your virtual date with this colonist girl . . .

ALAN: Melanie.

EDNA: . . . but I want you to take your friend Walter along. At least I'll know someone will be there with you in case of an emergency.

ALAN: There won't be any emergencies, Mom. But if it would make you feel any better . . .

EDNA: It would.

ALAN: I'll take Walter with me. *(He stands.)* I'd better go tell him we're going to Jupiter Park tonight. Thanks!

(He exits.)

LORI: Dad, is Alan's new girlfriend some kind of criminal?

WILLIAM: Of course not, honey. I'm sure she's a perfectly nice girl. Even if she *does* live on Io.

(William, Edna, and Lori stare at their computer screens and eat in silence as the curtain slowly falls.)

ACT TWO

The curtain opens on the futuristic kitchen—albeit slightly less hi-tech than that in Scene One—of Melanie K44 and her family on the Io colony. Melanie's father, Bert, and her brother, Louis, are seated at the breakfast table. Father and son gaze intently at notebook-size computers built into the table. Her mother, Alice, stands before a wall panel with an empty juice glass in her hand.

ALICE: Does anyone want more juice?

BERT: *(holding out his glass without looking up from the computer screen)* Thanks.

(Alice pushes a button, and the wall panel slides open. She takes out a cylinder full of orange juice and fills her husband's glass.)

LOUIS: My teacher says that people on Earth used to get fruit from trees.

ALICE: Really? From trees?

LOUIS: What are trees, anyway?

ALICE: Some sort of plant they had on Earth a long time ago. I'm afraid that was a century or two before my time.

(Melanie enters and sits at the table as her mother fills her juice glass.)

MELANIE: What was before your time, Mom?

ALICE: Trees.

MELANIE: We learned about trees in school. They used to grow all over Earth before the Earthlings finally chopped them all down.

BERT: Do we really have to discuss Earth at the breakfast table? My grandparents saved every hundred-dollar coin they could scrape together just to get away from that awful planet, and I don't think we need to waste precious oxygen gabbing about it now.

LOUIS: What's a hundred-dollar coin?

ALICE: Never mind, dear. The point is that your great-grandparents suffered great hardships to travel across the solar system and build the great domes of Io so that generations to come wouldn't have to live on a polluted, war-torn world like Earth.

MELANIE: I don't think Earth is *all* bad. We were studying Earth history for Galactic Unity month—

BERT: What kind of trash are they teaching you kids in school these days? No one is going to convince me that there's *anything* good about Earth or the people who live on that horrible, filthy planet.

LOUIS: Have you ever been there, Dad?

BERT: Of course not! I wouldn't visit Earth for all the ice on Ganymede. I've met an Earthling or two in my time, though, and I can assure you that they're without doubt the most arrogant, ill-mannered, self-centered individuals this side of the Milky Way.

MELANIE: They can't *all* be like that.

ALICE: Don't argue with your father, Melanie. Especially when he's talking about Earth.

MELANIE: But Mom! Just because you meet a couple of Earthlings who aren't very nice, it doesn't mean everybody on Earth is no good. There are plenty of nasty characters on Io, but that doesn't mean all of us are bad.

BERT: And what makes you such an expert? How many Earthlings have *you* ever known?

MELANIE: None. At least, not yet.

BERT: What's that supposed to mean?

MELANIE: *(hesitantly)* Well, I have a date tonight—

LOUIS: A date? You mean, with a boy?

MELANIE: *(sarcastically)* No, Louis. With a Martian fire-worm.

ALICE: Anyone we know, dear?

MELANIE: Not really, Mom. He doesn't live around here.

BERT: A Jovian?

MELANIE: Actually, Dad, he lives on Earth.

BERT: If this is your idea of a joke, Melanie, I'm afraid I fail to see the humor in it.

MELANIE: No joke, Dad. My friend Jemma was scanning the SpaceNet, and she downloaded this holo-dating program—

BERT: *(angrily)* So you girls decided to key in.

MELANIE: It was just for fun! Anyway, they matched me up with this boy named Alan who lives on Earth, and I thought it might be fun—

BERT: I don't care what you thought! No daughter of mine is going out with an Earthling!

MELANIE: But, Dad! It's only a virtual date! I'll be safe in my room with the VR machine the whole time. We're going to run "Jupiter Park."

ALICE: *(to Bert)* I understand that's a very safe program.

BERT: *(to Alice)* Who's side are you on, anyway?

ALICE: It's not a question of sides, dear. I just don't see the harm in letting Melanie meet this boy in Virtual Reality. Let her see for herself what Earthlings are like.

BERT: All right, Melanie. I still don't like it, but I know when I'm outnumbered. You're not going alone, though. If you're determined to do this thing, take Jemma along with you. At least someone will be around to unplug you if anything goes wrong.

MELANIE: *(jumping up and hugging her parents)* Thanks, you two! Everything will be fine. You'll see! I'd better go tell Jemma. *(She gulps down her juice and exits.)*

LOUIS: Why would Melanie even want to go on a date with some stupid Earthling, anyway?

BERT: Drink your juice, son.

(The curtain falls.)

ACT THREE

The curtain rises on the impressive main gate of Jupiter Park. Everything is slightly simplified—edges are rounded off and small details such as leaves on trees are missing. The gate, the volcanoes in the background, and the benches on either side of the gate all seem slightly bigger and brighter than life, reminding us that the entire set is a Virtual Reality construct. The overall effect is one of a tropical island in a Disney film. Melanie and Jemma enter.

JEMMA: This is amazing, Mel. It almost feels real!

MELANIE: It *is* real, Jemma. At least, it's real for *us*.

JEMMA: As long as we stay plugged in, that is. It's hard to believe we're still sitting in your room on Io.

MELANIE: Don't think about it, Jem. It's more fun if you just forget about the machine and let things happen.

JEMMA: I'll try. *(She looks at her ringwatch.)* Shouldn't the Earthling be here by now?

MELANIE: His name is Alan, and yes, he was supposed to load the program and click on "Main Gate" at 20:30 Solar Standard Time.

JEMMA: It's almost 20:45 already. My dad says you just can't count on Earthlings to do what they *say* they're going to do.

MELANIE: My folks say the same thing. Maybe dating a boy from Earth isn't such a great idea after all.

JEMMA: Are you kidding? How often do a couple of girls from Io ever get to meet a real, live Earthling face-to-face?

MELANIE: I just hope my parents are wrong about the Earthlings.

JEMMA: Parents are almost always wrong about everything, Mel. You should know that by now.

(The girls sit on one of the benches near the main gate.)

MELANIE: Maybe Alan thought we were supposed to meet at the East Gate. I'd better go check.

JEMMA: Go ahead. I'll wait here in case he shows up late.

MELANIE: Thanks, Jem. I'll be back in a few minutes.

JEMMA: Don't worry about it. *(As Melanie exits, Jemma takes a tiny computer out of her shoulder bag.)* I'll just download that new cyberzine everyone's been talking about.

(While Jemma reads, Alan and Walter enter from the other side.)

WALTER: Sorry I was late.

ALAN: That's okay, Walter. I just hope Melanie doesn't think I stood her up.

WALTER: *(noticing Jemma)* Is that she?

ALAN: No. I saw a hologram of Melanie on the SpaceNet. That girl must be part of the program.

WALTER: She looks awfully nice for someone who isn't even real. I think I'll go talk to her.

ALAN: Go ahead. I'm going to check out the West Gate. Maybe Melanie is looking for me. *(He exits. Walter sits down next to Jemma.)*

WALTER: Hi.

JEMMA: Oh, hi. You must be—

WALTER: Walter.

(He holds out his hand, and Jemma shakes it.)

JEMMA: Oh. I thought . . . Well, never mind. I'm Jemma.

WALTER: Do you work here?

JEMMA: What do you mean?

WALTER: Are you, like, a guide or something?

JEMMA: No. Are you?

WALTER: Of course not. I'm real.

JEMMA: So am I.

WALTER: You can't be. What are you doing in this program if you're real?

JEMMA: I was about to ask you the same question.

WALTER: I plugged in with my friend, Alan. He has a date with some girl from Io.

JEMMA: Melanie.

WALTER: Right. Melanie. How did you know?

JEMMA: Melanie's my best friend. She brought me along in case the Earthling . . .

WALTER: In case the Earthling *what*?

JEMMA: Nothing. I'm sorry.

WALTER: Are you really from Io?. You're not at all what I expected someone from Io to look like.

JEMMA: You're not exactly what I imagined an

Earthling would be like, either. My parents always say . . . *(She stops, and they both smile.)*

WALTER: That's all right. My parents say the same thing about your people. Have you been inside the park yet?

JEMMA: No. Have you?

WALTER: Not yet. Do you want to go in?

JEMMA: *(glancing at her ringwatch)* Why not? I'm sure our wandering pals will catch up with each other sooner or later.

(Walter stands and offers Jemma his hand. She takes it, and, together, they pass through the gate. A moment later, Melanie enters.)

MELANIE: Jemma? *(She exits in search of her friend just as Alan enters from the other side.)*

ALAN: Walter? *(He exits just as Melanie returns. She looks at her ringwatch and then sits on the bench. Alan enters and sees her.)* Melanie?

MELANIE: Alan? *(She stands just as he sits down. He quickly stands as Melanie sits back down. She jumps to her feet before Alan can sit again.)*

ALAN: Sorry I'm late.

MELANIE: That's okay. I'm glad you're here.

ALAN: Me, too.

MELANIE: *(after a long, awkward pause)* So you're from Earth.

ALAN: That's right. And you're from Io.

MELANIE: Fourth generation.

ALAN: Really? You seem so . . . *(He stops, embarrassed.)*

MELANIE: So *what*?

ALAN: Well, *normal*.

MELANIE: Why wouldn't I be normal?

ALAN: I don't know. My parents say that people from Io are . . . I don't know. Different.

MELANIE: I guess we *are* different in some ways. We don't have crime and air pollution like you do on Earth.

ALAN: And we don't have shortages of water and oxygen like you do on Io. My little sister says . . .

MELANIE: You have a sister? How old is she?

ALAN: Nine.

MELANIE: My little brother is nine, too.

ALAN: Really? I always wanted a brother.

MELANIE: I always wanted a little sister.

ALAN: *(joking)* Maybe we could arrange a trade sometime. Just for a little while, of course.

MELANIE: I don't think so! My parents don't even like the idea of my *dating* an Earthling, not to mention bringing one home. They're very sweet, but they're kind of old-fashioned when it comes to people who are, well—

ALAN: Different?

MELANIE: Yes. Different.

ALAN: My folks are the same way. My mom said I

121

couldn't even come here tonight unless I brought a friend along.

MELANIE: Really? My dad said the exact same thing! Maybe the SpaceNet is matching parents along with us.

ALAN: I bet they are.

(Walter and Jemma, holding hands, appear from behind the main gate.)

WALTER: *(to Alan and Melanie)* Hey! Where have you guys been? The big volcano is going to erupt in five minutes!

ALAN: *(gazing at Melanie, with obvious interest)* We'll catch you two later.

(Walter and Jemma run off through the gate to the park, hand in hand. Melanie shyly studies Alan.)

MELANIE: So what's it like?

ALAN: What?

MELANIE: Having all the oxygen you could ever want on your planet.

ALAN: We . . . don't even think about it.

MELANIE: We got to order extra canisters from Ceres, especially during the athletic Olympics season!

ALAN: Really?

MELANIE: Yeah, and if they don't get shipped on time, all the competitions that require a lot of exertion are canceled.

ALAN: *(trying to be comforting)* That must be tough.

MELANIE: What do you do for fun on Earth?

ALAN: I'm mostly into water sports. I do a lot of skin-diving in the syntha-lakes.

MELANIE: Syntha-lakes? What are they?

ALAN: Well, there's Great Lake 1 and 2. Then there are the Little Lakes and Streams System, built on the original locations.

MELANIE: What do you mean?

ALAN: Oh, didn't you know? All of Earth's original lakes and streams were destroyed by something called acid rain a couple of centuries ago. So they built new ones that weren't polluted. They had to start with gases and reconstruct them on a molecular level.

MELANIE: Fake water? What's it like?

ALAN: About the same as the real thing, I guess. Just a little stickier. Hey, I've got a great idea! Why don't we check out the Time Travel Museum? I hear it's got some great Ancient Earth exhibits.

(The two disappear through the gate, hand in hand.)

ACT FOUR

The curtain rises on the Time Travel Museum, a dark space with lifelike dioramas, as in New York's Museum of Natural History. Alan and Melanie are gawking at a huge orange tree, covered with large oranges.

MELANIE: What is it, Alan? *(Alan squints at the label beneath the tree.)*

ALAN: Something that used to grow on Earth: an orange tree.

(He picks an orange and peels it. He takes a whiff of it and his face lights up. Then he pops a segment of the orange into his mouth.)

ALAN: Umm . . . Try it!

MELANIE: *(frightened)* But Dad says there's a lot of pollution on Earth . . . Maybe it'll be bad for me . . .

ALAN: Melanie, it's only a historical virtual orange!

(Melanie takes a segment and hesitantly bites into it.)

MELANIE: Wow! Wonder if I could download a crate of these things for later!

ALAN: C'mon, there's supposed to be a twentieth-century wilderness trail up ahead!

(The two start off.)

MELANIE: Ever hear about dome-surfing?

ALAN: What's that?

MELANIE: All the kids on Io are into it. You rent these antigravity boards and surf along the edges of the dome.

ALAN: Really?

MELANIE: I'll download you a dome-surfer simulator through SpaceNet.

ALAN: Who knows, I might even make it to Io some day to try the *real* thing.

(He takes her hand as they disappear offstage and the curtain falls.)

READING FOR UNDERSTANDING

Act One

1. How has technology changed breakfast on Earth? Do you think that this could happen?
2. Does Alan remind you of today's teenagers? Why or why not?
3. How do Alan's parents feel about the colonists of Io? Do you think they are being fair?

Act Two

4. How are Melanie's and Alan's families similar?
5. Why do Melanie's parents resent people who live on Earth?

Act Three

6. What does Alan say that proves he is prejudiced against people from Io?
7. Is Melanie prejudiced against Earthlings? How do you know?
8. Why doesn't Alan go with his friend to see the volcano?
9. Could these events happen in the future?
10. Could Earth ever be the way Alan describes it?

Act Four

11. What do Alan and Melanie learn that brings them closer together?
12. What does Alan say about seeing Melanie in person?
13. Would you like to try virtual reality?

RESPONDING TO THE PLAY

1. What do you think of a world controlled by computers? What advantages would there be? What disadvantages?

2. Do you think dating in the future will be different from the way people date now? What might some of the differences be? What might some of the similarities be?

REVIEWING VOCABULARY

Match each word on the left with the correct definition on the right.

1. orbit
2. downloaded
3. colonize
4. cylinder
5. hologram
6. virtual reality
7. dioramas
8. interplanetary

a. three-dimensional photo
b. to settle
c. shape with two equal sides and a curved surface
d. to circle around
e. between planets
f. transferred from one computer to another
g. lifelike models
h. artificial reality created with computer sensors to duplicate experience

THINKING CRITICALLY ABOUT CULTURE

1. Describe how technology affects the way people meet and work together in your community.

2. How can we use technology to improve relations among people? To make the world a closer and more cooperative community?

3. In this play, even real oranges and eggs are rare. What do we lose in our trend toward "superfast" food? What do we gain?

4. Make a list of things on Earth that Alan might "download" to Melanie. What would he share with her? When you finish, list the things he might not want to share.

WRITING PROJECTS

1. Write a one-act, one-scene sequel to this play in which Melanie meets Alan's family for the first time. Write dialogue and stage directions. Make your play funny and lively.

2. Imagine that you are flying above the Earth. What do you see and feel? Write your feelings in the form of a poem.

3. Research simulators at your library. Then present a report to the class.

Tendar Fever

Sandra Widener

In H.G. Wells's novel The War of the Worlds, invaders from outer space attack Earth. The situation for humans seems hopeless. Suddenly, the invaders are stopped in their tracks. They are killed by the germs of the common cold.

Scientists now worry about astronauts bringing new diseases from outer space. In Tendar Fever, the play you are about to read, a deadly disease spreads on Earth. It may be from outer space.

The worst thing about an epidemic can be the fear it causes. Fear combined with ignorance brings panic. Decency and good sense seem lost in the confusion.

It takes a special kind of courage to keep a level head under such conditions. Voni, the main character in Tendar Fever, has just this kind of courage. But will her courage alone be enough to save her?

VOCABULARY WORDS

lethal (LEE-thuhl) deadly; fatal
❖ The new viral disease may cause a *lethal* epidemic.

hysteria (hih-STEHR-ee-uh) outbreak of wild fear or excitement
❖ When news of the epidemic became known, there was an outbreak of mass *hysteria*.

carriers (KAR-ee-uhrz) people who can pass a contagious disease on to others
❖ *Carriers* of typhoid fever may not even be aware that they have it.

genetic (juh-NEHT-ihk) having to do with heredity
❖ Through research, scientists hope to find the cure for many *genetic* diseases.

grapple (GRAP-uhl) to struggle in a hand-to-hand fight
❖ We saw the wrestler *grapple* to pin his opponent down.

KEY WORD

enzymes (EHN-zymez) proteins in plant or animal cells that cause specific chemical reactions
❖ The *enzymes* in plant and animal cells usually become inactive at high temperatures.

CHARACTERS

Mort Fissel, *astronaut*
Stacey Jordan, *astronaut*
Voni King, *astronaut*
Jasmine Mabewe, *astronaut*
Three astronauts
Engineer
Official
Man 1 on TV
Man 2 on TV
Woman on TV
Man 1
Man 2
Woman 1
Woman 2

SETTING

Act One
The astronaut isolation chamber on Earth

Act Two
The astronauts' apartment on Earth in the domed community of Kanos

Act Three
Scene 1
The astronauts' apartment and in the streets of Kanos

Scene 2
The apartment, one week later

Scene 3
The streets and underground passages of Kanos

ACT ONE

Inside the astronaut isolation chamber *on Earth. Astronauts remain here for two weeks after returning from missions to other planets. Doctors and scientists examine them to make sure they have not contracted anything that might be harmful to Earthlings or to Earth's domed atmosphere. The room is white and spotless. There is one window with a view to the parched landscape outside. Everyone now lives inside domed communities because global warming made living on Earth almost impossible. Global warming has melted enough of the polar ice to thaw long-dormant viruses. This problem, plus viruses brought back to Earth by astronauts, has resulted in mass epidemics on Earth. Some of these epidemics have killed large numbers of people. The possibility of new epidemics is a source of widespread fear. The astronauts' home is Kanos, a community of farms, schools, businesses, and playgrounds—all under a plastic dome.*

The seven astronauts in the sparsely furnished room returned two weeks ago from a visit to the planet Tendar. It was a scientific expedition to gather plants that scientists suspected could help cure Jag's Disease. This is a new viral disease that may have originated on Tendar and that now may cause another lethal epidemic.

As the scene opens, some astronauts are working with microscopes and papers. Others are playing games or watching television and looking bored. Duffel bags are piled near the door because the astronauts are to be released tonight.

MORT: *(peering through a microscope)* Fascinating!

STACEY: *(walking over to him in interest)* What did you find? Does the plant look promising?

MORT: It sure does, Stacey. *(pointing to a red plant with spikes near the microscope)* This spiny little monster looks like the answer to everyone's prayers. At least, anyone who's ever had Jag's Disease.

STACEY: Let me see. *(She bends over and looks into the microscope.)* Look at that! The enzymes in that plant are destroying the virus.

MORT: It was a hunch on Voni's part. But I had a feeling that she was right and that Tendar's dogtooth plant might do the trick. This is great.

STACEY: *(She turns to the room and cups her hands around her mouth.)* Hey, everyone! It looks like it's going to work! Take a look at this!

(The six other astronauts crowd around and take turns peering through the microscope.)

VONI: Unbelievable. We were all hoping, but who knew it would really work?

JASMINE: I think some celebrating is in order.

STACEY: How many were there at last count—I mean, people who have Jag's Disease?

MORT: Thousands. All they're going to need now is a simple shot—after all the other tests are done, of course. But right now, it looks great.

STACEY: *(looking out the window)* What will look great to me is freedom.

JASMINE: Not much longer to wait. This evening, we're out of here. I can't wait to get out of this room and give my kids a hug.

VONI: At least you're married and have someone to go home to. You're the only one of us who does. Is it hard being gone so long?

JASMINE: Of course. But when you think that your work makes a difference, it's hard to say no. Hey, you must feel great right now. Didn't you think your idea was a bit of a long shot?

VONI: I always believed in it. I just had to convince the people with the money that the research would be worthwhile.

(There is a knock on the door.)

ENGINEER: *(He opens the door, which leads to an out-door scene—except it's all under the dome.)* You ready to rejoin civilization?

STACEY: Ready? I'll say!

ENGINEER: Come on out.

STACEY: *(She grabs her duffel bag, puts it over her shoulder, walks outside the room, and takes a deep breath.)* Ah! The canned air of Kanos! This is great.

MORT: *(following her out, looking around)* You're too young to remember real air. Even this air is better than being inside that room, though.

STACEY: Come on, Voni. Let's go home. *(calling over her shoulder)* See you all in the lab next week.

MORT: See you, Stace. Call if you get bored this week-end.

STACEY: Bored? That's not likely. I haven't seen James in five months. We're supposed to get married, but his mother is sick with Jag's Disease, and he can't leave her for a minute.

MORT: 'Till next week then.

(*Mort walks off alone. Jasmine is greeted by her family, two boys and a husband. Voni and Stacey walk off in another direction.*)

ACT TWO

The living room in Stacey and Voni's apartment in Kanos, two months after their release from the isolation chamber. The walls are white and covered with art museum posters. The overstuffed chairs and a sofa are beige. There is a huge TV set on one wall that is constantly on. Along another wall is a chemistry lab. There are test tubes, beakers, complicated little machines, a microscope. Stacey is sitting and watching the TV when Voni comes in.

STACEY: So what's the latest?

VONI: (*shaking her head*) Nobody knows anything. I can't believe it. Mort dead. Jasmine dead. It's almost too much to take in. It's like having your family die. And you don't even know if you're going to be next. And then there's that idiot. (*Voni points to the TV.*)

MAN ON TV: . . . round them up. It's only a matter of time. They'll infect us all! Put them somewhere where they can't kill us, too!

VONI: He's still at it?

STACEY: (*sighing*) Oh, you bet. That idiot would have us all torpedoed into space if he had his way. Of course, there's no mention of the cure for Jag's

Disease we found. No mention that we know almost nothing about whatever it is that killed Mort and Jasmine and her family. We don't even know if we really brought it back from Tendar.

VONI: None of that matters when hysteria gets going. I can understand it, though. It is scary. At least the experiments are going well. I'm close, really close to finding out what caused Mort and Jasmine's deaths. I almost have it, and it looks like it did come from Tendar. And it looks like we were all exposed. There are traces in our blood.

STACEY: *(anxiously)* You didn't tell me that! Are we going to get it, too? I mean, everyone who's gotten this—this whatever it is—has died or is dying.

MAN ON TV: . . . just confirmed. Another innocent victim, this one merely a friend of the astronauts. Dead. How much more do we have to take? Put them away! Now! For good!

VONI: Shut that thing off!

STACEY: Come on, Voni. I want to know what's going on. How else are we going to find out? But first, tell me more about what you found out! Tell me!

(There is a knock at the door.)

OFFICIAL: Open up.

(Stacey and Voni look at each other, alarmed.)

VONI: Who's out there?

OFFICIAL: Health Institute.

VONI: *(She opens the door.)* Come in.

(The official enters with two others, one man, one

136

*woman. All are wearing white baggy suits that cover
their bodies, with clear bubble masks covering their
heads.)*

OFFICIAL: Sorry to bother you. We need to talk. You've
heard about your friends? The other astronauts?

VONI: *(angrily)* Of course. We went to their funerals.
And we didn't need to wear any spacesuits, either.

OFFICIAL: Maybe you should have. You may have
caught Tendar Fever from them.

VONI: Tendar Fever? Who's calling it that? Who are
you, anyway? What gives you the right to barge in
here?

OFFICIAL: The Health Institute gives us the right. It
looks like we've got a serious outbreak on our hands.
The latest figures don't look good.

VONI: *(alarmed)* Latest figures? What latest figures?

OFFICIAL: As of this afternoon, we've had fifty-five
deaths. All traceable to contact with the astronauts—
that is, those of you who went to Tendar. We need to
take some blood now. Please.

*(Voni and Stacey silently offer their arms while the
officials take blood samples.)*

OFFICIAL: *(as though reciting from memory)* You are
hereby restricted to this apartment. Please do not
attempt to leave. You may call a store for delivery of
food and other necessities. All deliveries should be left
outside the door. Do not have any direct contact with
anyone else. *(relaxing a bit)* Sorry, but until we get
this under control, you're too dangerous to let out.
We'll let you know when we have more information.

137

STACEY: *(sarcastically, under her breath)* Oh, gee, thanks.

OFFICIAL: *(turning at the door)* This is for your protection, too. There are some angry people out there who'd like to see you put in isolation—or worse. At least in here you'll be safe.

(The officials leave, shutting the door behind them.)

STACEY: Safe? What's he talking about?

MAN 1 ON TV: So you say we should round them up and put them in a specially built dome?

STACEY: *(turning to the TV)* What's that?

WOMAN ON TV: That's right. Safer for them, and safer for us. We can't let these carriers loose. This is an outbreak that threatens every person on Earth.

MAN 2 ON TV: This is a plot! Those astronauts brought this back because they think there are too many people on Earth. It's a twisted population-control scheme, and the astronauts are behind it! Round them up all right—and then kill them!

MAN 1 ON TV: Now, now, calm down. We don't need to go that far. But I agree—whatever happened, these astronauts need to be rounded up and taken away from the rest of us.

STACEY: *(still staring at the TV)* Can you believe this? It's frightening. They sound like they think we did it on purpose! As if we weren't infected ourselves!

VONI: People are scared. They don't know what to do.

(Suddenly, there is banging on the door.)

MAN 1: *(speaking from outside the door)* Killers! Come out so we can kill you first!

MAN 2: *(also outside the door)* I've got the fever, and I'm going to die! And you gave it to me!

STACEY: *(shouting)* We did nothing to you! Our friends have died too!

VONI: We have lasers. If you break down that door, I'll shoot!

MAN 2: Cowards! You're cowards as well as killers! *(The pounding stops, and there is the sound of footsteps running away.)*

VONI: *(sitting down)* That shook me up.

STACEY: *(staring at the TV screen)* Voni, I just checked the mail. Listen to this. *(She reads from the screen.)* "Get out, murderers. Go back to your death planet." And this one: "You deserve to die for killing so many." There are more messages. Lots more. They can't really think we meant to do this, can they? We went through the biofilters, we stayed in the isolation room just like all other astronauts—

VONI: I told you. They're scared. The only thing we can do now is work on the cure. I've got the equipment here to do that—it won't work as well as the lab, but I can do it. The sooner we find a cure, the sooner people will get well and life can begin again.

ACT THREE, SCENE 1

Stacey and Voni's apartment, two weeks later. The TV is still on.

STACEY: *(hugging herself)* It's so lonely now. It seems to be getting colder, too. Do you think they shut off the heat when they moved everyone else out of the building?

VONI: *(shifting her attention between her microscope and a notebook computer)* What?

STACEY: Oh, never mind. It's just that sometimes this feels like a death sentence. I mean, we know *we* aren't going to get sick, but being alone like this is so hard.

VONI: *(looking up at Stacey)* It could be harder. Thousands of people have died.

STACEY: *(hurriedly)* I know, I know, Voni. I do feel lucky to be alive. It's been so hard.

VONI: *(looking back into the microscope)* My real fear is that the food will run out, and the systems will start to go because there aren't enough engineers to keep the air flowing and the dome repaired. Everything that keeps us alive depends on people.

STACEY: I know. I'm sorry, Voni. I sound like a spoiled brat.

VONI: The good news is that I'm closer than ever. The big clue to this puzzle is that we *didn't* get sick when so many others did.

STACEY: What do you mean?

VONI: Some people can resist this virus, and others

140

can't. Maybe it's genetic, and I'm close to finding it if that is so. If I do, I can create the cure.

MAN ON TV: . . . no cure in sight. Doctors are working around the clock to find an answer. Today's death total: one hundred ninety-five. Total since the fever began: fifteen thousand, eight hundred and seventy-nine dead. Officials have begun to voice worry about the supplies of milk and vegetables . . .

STACEY: *(bitterly)* Sometimes I feel like telling you not to bother. Since this started, people want to *kill* us! They blame us! Why save them, anyway?

VONI: I know you're not serious, so I won't answer that. But if you want to look at it selfishly, it's the only way we can get our lives back. If, for instance, you ever want to see James again.

STACEY: Thank God he hasn't gotten it yet. I talked to him yesterday and told him if we ever got out of here, I was really going to marry him.

VONI: *(smiling as she looks into the microscope)* Let's hope he's one of the lucky people who can resist the disease.

(There is a thud as a heavy object lands against the plastic window in the living room.)

VONI: Thank goodness they don't make windows out of glass any more. *(excitedly, as she taps away at the keyboard of her notebook computer)* Stacey, I can't believe it! Why didn't it ever occur to me before? It's the air tankers!

STACEY: What are you talking about?

VONI: I was just looking through the patient histories.

Every single person who died from the fever was at one of those locations. They died. But even their close family members didn't get the disease.

STACEY: So?

VONI: Come! Look! *(She impatiently motions Stacey over to the computer.)* The fever is not contagious. It was something in the environments where these people happened to be! Check this out! Every one of those locations in the dome was using air-supply tankers from the same company, Breathe-Free Industries!

STACEY: But what about all our astronaut friends who died?

VONI: *(motioning to the screen)* Take a look, would you? The astronaut isolation chamber was ordering air tankers from Breathe-Free, too! You had to be exposed to it for a certain length of time. That's why there are only traces in our blood and we're not sick.

STACEY: Then we're not contagious?

VONI: No!

STACEY: Let's get ready. We've got work to do!

(Voni turns the TV off and moves her chair toward Stacey as the lights dim.)

ACT THREE, SCENE 2

The apartment, one hour later.

VONI: Do we have everything?

STACEY: Documents, check. Lasers, check. What else do we need?

VONI: The false "cure," in case we end up trapped. *(She tosses a test tube of colored liquid into her pocket.)*

STACEY: Do you think anyone is going to recognize us?

VONI: Well, our picture has been on all the news networks, with the other astronauts. But if you want the truth, I think everyone's only thinking about trying to survive at this point.

STACEY: Okay, then. Let's go.

(The two women leave, locking the door behind them. They walk cautiously through the empty, well-lit halls of the apartment building and leave it.)

ACT THREE, SCENE 3

A street in Kanos. The buildings are high-tech and very plain. High, square entrances seem to have no doors. Below the street, we see a cross section of an underground passage with a stairway entrance from a manhole on the street.

VONI: You see anyone?

STACEY: No. It's so spooky in there.

VONI: Stay close. It's spooky out here, too.

(Suddenly, a mob of people runs from behind a building toward Stacey and Voni.)

WOMAN 1: There they are! Get them!

STACEY: *(looking panicked)* Now what?

VONI: *(breathlessly, as she begins to run)* Come on! We've got to run if we're going to live longer than the five minutes it'll take them to catch up with us!

(Stacey and Voni run in the opposite direction from the mob. Then Stacey opens a manhole cover in the street and begins to climb down.)

VONI: *(panting)* Where are you going?

STACEY: I know this place. I did some work here years ago. It leads to a tunnel that will take us out near the lab. Get down here! Follow me!

VONI: I'm right behind you.

(Voni shuts the manhole cover. A few minutes later, Voni and Stacey can hear the sound of many running feet above them.)

STACEY: This way.

VONI: How can you tell? It's black down here.

STACEY: I think I'm remembering right. I'm pretty sure this will work.

VONI: Okay, I'm with you. *(She stumbles and falls.)* Ouch! What was that?

STACEY: Probably the tracks. Feel along the wall here. That's the best way. *(Behind them, a light flickers in the distance, and the two hear muted voices.)*

VONI: *(tensely)* They figured out where we went.

STACEY: Let's see . . . *(She and Voni stop running. Stacey frowns and bites her lip. Then she snaps her fingers.)* Bedrock. The bedrock tunnel.

VONI: Where—and what—is that?

STACEY: *(points to the ground)* There. It's a tunnel the engineers used to—oh, just follow me!

(Stacey leads the way to a trap door on the floor. She

144

opens it with great effort and lowers herself down on the ladder.)

VONI: You think I'm going *there*?

STACEY: You want to stay here and die like a rat?

(Voni looks at her, shakes her head, and follows Stacey down. At the bottom of the ladder is an opening that is slightly wider than a narrow crawl space. It opens to the left and right and follows the length of the tracks. Stacey and Voni kneel in the muddy puddle on the dirt floor, crowded together. After a few seconds, they hear footsteps above and then voices.)

WOMAN 1: You see where they go?

MAN 1: Where can they go? If we follow this, we'll find them.

WOMAN 2: Wait. There used to be a tunnel even farther below this. Now, where was that?

(Stacey and Voni exchange terrified glances. Stacey motions to the crawl spaces on either side of the puddle in which they've been kneeling, and the two move into them.)

MAN 1: *(triumphantly as he pulls open the trap door)* There! *(He shines a flashlight into the puddle, where footsteps are visible.)* Hey! Over here! We've got them!

(A group of people, including Man 1 and Women 1 and 2, descend the ladder. Voni and Stacey are desperately trying to move farther into the narrow crawl space.)

WOMAN 1: I can squeeze in there. I'll get them. *(She begins to follow Voni. Another woman follows Stacey.)*

WOMAN 2: Got you, you killer! *(She drags Voni roughly*

out into the area by the ladder and pushes her up the ladder.) We're going to kill you!

VONI: If you kill me, you won't know how to use the cure!

WOMAN 2: What cure?

VONI: *(lying)* The cure for Tendar Fever. We're on the way to the lab with it now.

MAN 1: What if she's right? Get her up onto the street. *(to Voni)* Go on, killer.

WOMAN 2: *(deep in the crawl space. Her voice is muffled.)* Get out, you worm! *(She pushes Stacey out of the crawl space.)*

MAN 1: Go on. Up there. *(He points above, to the street.)*

STACEY: You're wrong. You're so wrong.

WOMAN 1: Wrong about what? Wrong that our children are dead and our husbands? Wrong that you brought the fever? That you caused it?

STACEY: We did nothing! I swear!

(The mob pushes Stacey and Voni up onto the street and surrounds them.)

WOMAN 1: Kill them *now*! Then get the cure!

(The mob begins to shove Stacey and Voni. A man and a woman begin to hit them. Suddenly, Voni pulls a test tube from her pocket.)

VONI: Stop! Now! Or I'll break this. I swear I will! Get away from me!

(Suddenly, the crowd is quiet and still. Then a man charges Voni.)

MAN 1: Give me that!

(He and Voni struggle for the test tube. Voni tosses it as far away as she can. It sails over the mob. All of them run for it. They struggle to grab the test tube, pushing each other out of the way. Man 1 gets it first.)

WOMAN 2: He got it! Now *I'm* going to die! *(She turns on the man and begins to attack him.)* You—you—

(The man and woman grapple with each other. The rest of the mob gathers around them, trying to grab the vial. The vial falls out of the man's hands, and this time it shatters on the ground.)

VONI: *(whispering)* Stacey! Now!

(The two begin running down the street together. They enter a building and bar the door.)

STACEY: *(gasping for breath)* Fools! Idiots!

VONI: *(also gasping for breath)* It's all right now. Our hoax worked. They'll be so busy trying to scoop up that sugar syrup from the sidewalk that they'll lose sight of us.

STACEY: Unbelievable. I should have known. You're going to save everyone despite themselves.

VONI: People aren't always like they've been since the fever. You know that. There are decent people, like James, and all our friends who never blamed us— plenty of other people, too, who never thought it was right, what happened to us.

STACEY: *(with disbelief)* You're so forgiving.

VONI: Realistic. People can be more mean and short sighted than any animals. But remember: People also tried to shield us when the mob wanted to break down our door. It's normal human behavior, if you know what I mean.

STACEY: I'll take *your* human behavior.

VONI: Thank you.

STACEY: *(after a moment)* I wonder where James is. I haven't seen him in so long . . .

VONI: *(looking outside)* I don't think they're following us any more. Come on, Stace. We've got to get to Breathe-Free Industries and stop them from shipping the last of those tankers! Then we've got to make sure the networks broadcast the truth as soon as possible!

(The two young women dash off into the street.)

READING FOR UNDERSTANDING

Overview

1. Two women astronauts race against time to find a cure for Tendar Fever. Who are they? What threats do they face? What do they decide to do at the end of the play?

Act I

2. Why do people on Earth live inside domed communities?

3. What was the purpose of the mission to Tendar? Did the astronauts find what they were looking for?

Act II

4. What happened to Mort and Jasmine?

5. Why do officials from the Health Institute visit Voni and Stacey? According to the officials, what must the women do now?

6. How do the statements from the people on television establish a tense atmosphere in this act?

Act III

7. At the beginning of this act, what do you think is Voni's real fear?

8. According to Voni, what is the key to finding a cure for Tendar Fever?

9. Why does the crowd pursue Stacey and Voni? Why do you think the man charges Voni and they struggle?

10. How does Voni arrange for their escape from the crowd? According to Voni, why is the struggle to save people still worthwhile?

RESPONDING TO THE PLAY

1. Pick out one scene, event, or statement that made an impression on you as you read. What about that scene or statement made it meaningful to you? Explain in a paragraph.
2. This play takes place some time in the distant future. Are there any events or characters that remind you of problems or people in today's world? Explain in a brief paragraph.

REVIEWING VOCABULARY

Match each word on the left with the correct definition on the right.

1. hysteria   **a.** having to do with heredity
2. genetic   **b.** infected people
3. grapple   **c.** wild fear
4. lethal   **d.** to struggle
5. carriers   **e.** deadly

THINKING CRITICALLY

1. How does this play suggest that new scientific advances may carry a high price? What kinds of results does scientific exploration have in the play?
2. The play also suggests that people's fears can cause them to behave cruelly. Give some examples of this kind of behavior from the play.
3. The officials say that the Health Institute gives them the right to barge in on Stacey and Voni and to restrict them to their apartment. Do you think society has the right to isolate people and to deprive them of liberty in this way? When might such actions be justified, if ever?
4. Voni says that people can be mean and

shortsighted, but they can also be decent and stand up for the right. Do you agree with Voni's outlook on "normal" human behavior? Explain your position.

5. What do you think will happen as the story continues? Will Voni and Stacey succeed in "saving everyone despite themselves"? Explain your prediction.

WRITING PROJECT

Think up a sequel to *Tendar Fever*. Will Voni and Stacey succeed in curing the victims of the epidemic? You might try setting your scene for the sequel at the Health Institute. Write lines of dialogue for Voni, Stacey, and the Director of the Institute.

A Clash of Wills

Mary Canrobert

Imagine a time more than one hundred years in the future. What do you think life might be like? Would people still look and feel and act the way they do now?

Or would science and technology have helped create a world vastly different from the one you know today?

This play takes place in the year 2110, when people live and travel throughout the universe. You meet Tia and Stone, who are getting ready to compete in the Galactic Olympics on the planet Kinn. Tia is from Bast, a planet that forbids its people to show emotion. Stone is from Dole. Dolians are encouraged to feel and show emotion.

As you may guess, this is no ordinary Olympics, and Tia and Stone are not like the typical athletes of today. They are about to fight each other with laser swords. Tia and Stone also face a showdown over their very different views of the world. Read on to see who wins the final battle in A Clash of Wills.

VOCABULARY WORDS

laser (LAY-zuhr) a device that gives off a beam of light
❖ Today, *laser* surgery is common.

scalpel (SKAL-puhl) small, sharp knife used by a surgeon
❖ The doctor used a *scalpel* to cut through the skin.

artificial (ahr-tuh-FIHSH-uhl) not natural; made by humans
❖ The man's teeth looked so real that no one could tell they were *artificial*.

eliminated (ih-LIHM-uh-nayt-uhd) removed
❖ The baseball team was *eliminated* during the play-offs.

galaxy (GAL-uhk-see) a very large group of stars
❖ The spaceship traveled from one *galaxy* to another.

downfall (DOWN-fawl) a sudden fall from power; a heavy fall
❖ The leader's *downfall* was due to his cruelty.

KEY WORDS

microshields (MY-kroh-sheeldz) small plates that protect the sword fighters from laser beams.
❖ The doctor inserted *microshields* into the laser sword fighter's body.

positrons (PAH-zuh-trahnz) amounts of energy needed to power laser swords.
❖ Stone and Tia used their thoughts to create *positrons*.

CHARACTERS

Tia, *female laser sword fighter from Bast*
Coffus, *Tia's trainer, male*
Stone, *male laser sword fighter from Dole*
Ink, *Stone's trainer, male*
Tia's doctor, *male*
Stone's doctor, *female*
Stone's mother and sister
Two laser sword fighters
Three Olympic judges
An Olympic announcer
A groundskeeper

SETTING

Act One
Scene 1
Operating room on Bast

Scene 2
Same day; operating room on Dole

Act Two
One week later; laser sword fighters' training room on Bast

Act Three
Two days later; Galactic Olympics site on planet Kinn

Scene 1
The viewers' area

Scene 2
Same day, laser sword fighter's mat and viewers' area

Act Four
Next day; laser sword fighters' training room on Bast

ACT ONE, SCENE 1

A **high-tech operating room** *in the Bast Olympics training tower. Room includes a metal operating table center stage, a metal instrument table next to the operating table, and an eight-foot-tall archway downstage right that glows green. Walls have computer monitors and gray-tinted glass cabinets.*

Tia is lying face down on the operating table. She is awake and covered with surgical cloths. Using a pencil-size laser scalpel, the doctor is opening the skin on the back of Tia's ankle. Coffus stands at the doctor's left, watching the surgery. The conversation is businesslike.

DOCTOR: *(talking as he works)* I am going to insert eleven microshields. The first one will go into your left ankle. The shields are a little smaller than they used to be. *(holding up a nickel-sized piece of metal)* Just two centimeters wide. *(inserting microshield)* You shouldn't feel pain because you passed through the pain cancellation arch before surgery.

TIA: The left ankle is hard to reach with a laser sword. The only way I can hit Coffus's ankle during practice is by jumping behind him. You have to hit all the shields to win a fight. *(changing to a more relaxed tone)* By the way, this is Coffus. He's my trainer.

(Doctor nods at Coffus.)

COFFUS: *(leaning in close to watch the doctor work)* She's the fastest sword fighter I've ever trained. She leaps behind me before I know she is there. *(moving near to Tia, serious)* In just three days, you fight the galaxy's second-best laser sword fighter. Don't take anything for granted.

TIA: *(snobbishly)* And who is the number one fighter in the galaxy, Coffus?

COFFUS: You are, but you've never fought in the Olympics before, nor have you fought anyone from Dole. This will be the most important battle of your life.

DOCTOR: Turn over on your back. *(becoming less businesslike)* Why are all these shields necessary?

COFFUS: The microshields protect areas where a direct hit could end the fight—or worse. The first fighter to hit all the opponent's shields wins the fight.

TIA: So please make sure they're in exactly the right places. *(She turns over; doctor works at her throat.)* What's the Dolian man's name?

COFFUS: *(smirking)* You won't believe it. Stone. His name is Stone.

TIA: Tell me about this Stone. Is he as backward and foolish as all the other fighters in our galaxy?

COFFUS: *(throwing up his hands in disgust)* More so. Dole is not even a planet. It's a moon. He and his people used to live on the planet Frit. They were thrown off the planet when they refused to accept the way things were changing. Dolians actually believe in letting nature have its way. *(He shakes his head in disgust.)*

DOCTOR: *(inserting microshields on Tia's shoulders)* I cannot imagine the lack of skills of doctors on Dole. They don't start training until they've completed thirteen youth years! I was programmed to be a doctor before I was born and have received medical training since I was three. You and Tia were programmed to

157

be laser sword fighters and began your training at three. *(He inserts microshield at Tia's stomach.)*

TIA: So they live on some worthless little moon, do they? They disgust me! *(She sits up to watch doctor insert microshield on right knee.)*

COFFUS: *(excited)* Hold on to that disgust! The more hatred you feel toward anyone outside of Bast, the more energy you will produce to power your laser sword.

TIA: *(annoyed)* I know, Coffus. I *know*!

DOCTOR: *(to Coffus)* The first eight microshields are in place. Do you want the last three put over the heart or the brain?

COFFUS: The brain.

TIA: *(She lies down, and the doctor works at the top of her head.)* The brain is difficult to defend, but I'm sure that ignorant Dolian hasn't the physical ability to make head strikes anyway. He probably can't jump higher than a foot.

DOCTOR: My work is finished. Be warned, Tia, you will feel a sharp sting if your opponent hits one of your microshields.

TIA: *(sitting up)* No problem, Doctor, I plan to do all the stinging.

(Lights out.)

ACT ONE, SCENE 2

A comfortable-looking doctor's office on Dole. A large picture window at right. A couch in front of the window. Family pictures hang on walls. At left, bookshelves and a large wooden desk. A padded examining table is center stage with a metal instrument table next to it. Stone is lying on the examining table. All but Stone's head is covered with a white sheet. The doctor moves the sheet as she works on different areas of Stone's body. The conversation is conventional and as relaxed as is possible in a doctor's office.

DOCTOR: *(holding an old-fashioned scalpel)* I have injected a numbing liquid into all the areas of your body that will receive a microshield, Stone. *(smiling)* You should feel no pain. *(She cuts a small opening in Stone's throat.)*

STONE: In three days, I get to battle the best laser sword fighter on Bast, Doc. I can't wait to show this galaxy that it doesn't take artificial programming to make a good fighter.

DOCTOR: *(inserting a microshield at each shoulder)* Nor does it take training from the age of three to be a good doctor.

STONE: What do you mean?

DOCTOR: On Bast, children are taken from their mothers at age three to begin their training in a field chosen for them by Bast's rulers.

STONE: That's unfair! Children need to be around people who love them. And *they* should be able to decide what they want to be when they grow up.

DOCTOR: *(She inserts three microshields over Stone's*

heart.) I agree, but Bastons do not value emotions such as love and happiness. They think that serving their planet and its laws is all that's important. That's why our ancestors were exiled to this moon. They could not accept the way our old planet, Frit, was following Bast's example.

STONE: Do you mean that children on Bast don't know love and happiness?

DOCTOR: They do until they go to live in training villages when they are three. Then they are brainwashed to forget about such things. *(She moves to work over Stone's stomach.)*

STONE: Do you think they really forget?

DOCTOR: They must, or they would not continue the brainwashing. *(She moves to insert a microshield into Stone's right knee.)* They program themselves to have strong, healthy physical bodies, superior intelligence, and faithfulness to Bast's rulers.

STONE: What if someone does not turn out so perfect?

DOCTOR: Well, I don't know what happens to everyone who isn't perfect, but I do know that their laser sword fighters who don't earn at least a bronze medal at the Olympics are banished forever. They are beamed to another planet almost immediately. Turn onto your stomach, please. *(Stone turns over, and the doctor begins work over his kidneys.)*

STONE: That is incredible! They feel no kindness toward one another at all?

DOCTOR: *(moving to insert a microshield into his left ankle)* None.

STONE: *(puzzled)* I don't understand something. A laser sword fighter must create positive energy to fuel the sword.

DOCTOR: That's right.

STONE: The more positive thoughts, the more energy the sword has. Now, a laser beam needs two thousand positrons per second to reach its target. So, how do Bastons create enough positive thoughts if they don't know about love and kindness?

DOCTOR: *(She stops working.)* On Bast, being positive means hating anyone who is against Bast. It means supporting the planet's ways with unquestioning loyalty. If a Bast sword fighter thought about love and kindness, he would not be able to create positrons because such ideas are negative on Bast. People on Bast don't even smile at each other.

STONE: *(suddenly rising to a sitting position)* I'm going to win this fight, and I know exactly how!

DOCTOR: *(arranging instruments on her tray)* How?

STONE: I'll confuse her with kindness.

(Lights out.)

ACT TWO

The laser sword fighters' practice room in the Bast Olympics training tower. Bare walls. Round fighters' mat, nineteen feet in diameter, center stage. Two large video screens hang from the ceiling, one behind each fighter's head, so that the other fighter can see it. These are "thought boards": they describe fighters' emotions and indicate the numerical level of emotional intensity.

Tia and Coffus are preparing to practice laser sword fighting. They are each holding a laser sword and standing downstage center. Tia's laser sword is two feet long. The handle is cuffed, and the shaft is a dull white. When positrons are flowing, the shaft glows. Coffus's sword has no cuff, and the shaft is slightly wider.

COFFUS: *(giving two small plastic discs to Tia)* Here, Tia, stick these on your temples. Then the thought board can pick up what you're thinking and measure the number of positrons you are producing.

TIA: *(She places discs on temples and looks at Coffus.)* What's that thing? *(pointing at Coffus's sword)*

COFFUS: *(holding out his laser sword)* This is the sword I used in the 2106 Olympics. It helped me win the gold. If you can beat me while I'm using this sword *(pats his sword),* you can beat anybody in the galaxy.

(Laser sounds fill the air as they fight.)

TIA: Ouch, you got my knee! *(reaching for knee)* Gee, that doctor wasn't kidding about its stinging.

COFFUS: You whine like a Dolian. Get up and fight like a Baston! *(The fighting continues.)*

TIA: Have you ever met a Dolian?

COFFUS: No. Why do you ask?

TIA: I just think it's important for me to know what kind of person I'll be fighting.

COFFUS: Dolians are backward. Their ways are wrong. That's all you need to know. Do you remember learning in your history class how undeveloped Baston used to be before we entered the genetic technology age?

TIA: Yes. *(pausing from fighting)*

COFFUS: *(also pausing)* Dolians are still like that.

TIA: *(resuming fighting)* That's senseless!

(Tia's thought board reads senseless. *Her positron level is at 2100. She hits Coffus's throat, both lungs, right knee, and spins around to get his ankle.)*

TIA: *(still firing)* Looks like your old sword is ready to go back into the closet, Coffus.

COFFUS: *(angry at Tia's remark)* Oh, really. *(He leaps into the air and fires two perfect shots at Tia's head.)* Let's see you do that.

TIA: No problem! *(She goes into a spin and then leaps, striking all three of Coffus's head microshields.)*

COFFUS: *(putting down his sword)* Your fight with the Dolian is going to be child's play. My sources tell me he chose to put three of his microshields over his heart, instead of in his head.

TIA: *(sarcastically)* I guess he thinks the heart is more important than the brain.

COFFUS: *(rising to fight)* Let's continue.

TIA: *(dodging laser fire)* Our superiors will be pleased when I win the gold, won't they?

COFFUS: No one in Bast is ever pleased, Tia. You either do your job well or you don't. Period.

TIA: That doesn't seem right. We should be rewarded for a job well done. If I win the gold, I'll end up being a trainer the rest of my life, like you. That's it. Period.

COFFUS: *(offended)* Do you want to be coddled and babied like a two year old, Tia? You're no longer an infant who needs attention and praise from her mother. You're a grown Baston laser sword fighter!

(Tia's thought board flashes Mother! Mother! Mother! *Her positron reading is at 200, which is very low.)*

COFFUS: *(in Tia's face)* We are superior to every other living thing in this galaxy. That's all you need to think about! That, and the fact that you are the best laser sword fighter Bast has ever had.

(Coffus's thought board flashes Bast.*)*

TIA: *(feeling guilty)* You're right, Coffus. It was wrong of me to think about myself. I'm going to win the gold for Bast!

(Tia attacks Coffus with all her might, striking his stomach, then spinning behind him to take both his kidneys. Her thought board reads Bast. *Her positron level is at 2400.)*

(Lights out.)

ACT THREE, SCENE 1

The site of the 2110 Olympic games on planet Kinn. The viewers' area—center stage—is packed with fans. Everyone is quiet. Stone's mother and sister are sitting in the front row of the stands, talking to each other and looking around.

MOTHER: *(looking around)* I can't believe how quiet everyone is during these games. Why don't they cheer for their planet? We may struggle on Dole since we were forced to move there, but at least we're happy. We can laugh or scream or cry if we want to.

SISTER: *(pointing offstage right)* Oh, look, Mom! I see Stone. He's sitting with some other fighters from Dole. *(yelling and waving)* Hi, Stone.

MOTHER: *(sadly, wiping eyes with a tissue)* I'm so sorry your father did not live to see your brother make it to the Olympics. He would have been so proud. Did you know that your father won a gold medal in diving in the 2078 Olympics?

SISTER: *(smiling)* Of course I knew that, Mother, and I bet he didn't have wings like a bird either, did he? Remember last night at the opening games?

MOTHER: *(wide-eyed)* How can I forget? Runners with legs that start under their armpits, swimmers with webbed feet and hands, and what about those basketball players?

SISTER: The shortest one I saw had to be at least eight feet tall. There's no way Doles are going to win any medals against creatures that look like that.

MOTHER: *(stubbornly, and shaking her finger at her daughter)* I won't feel a bit bad if Dole loses. Those other planets have programmed their athletes to be like they are. It's not fair because it's not natural-born athletic ability.

SISTER: The Bastons look so cold and inhuman. At least the Dolians look happy and upbeat. *(waving again in Stone's direction)*

(Crowd murmurs and points toward front of viewers' area.)

MOTHER: *(looking around)* What's going on? Why is everyone talking all of a sudden?

SISTER: *(pointing in front of them)* Look out there, Mom. A male Baston just lost a laser sword match!

MOTHER: They're holding the shield over his head! The fighter is kneeling in front of them.

SISTER: He's disappeared!

MOTHER: But why? Why did they have to beam him away? Where did they send him?

SISTER: I don't know, Mom. He didn't fight so well. The Bastons won't tolerate that. *(She shakes her head sadly.)*

(Lights out.)

ACT THREE, SCENE 2

Round fighters' mat in front of crowded viewers' area. Thought boards hang from tall poles, one behind where each fighter will stand. Dolian fans take up a large section of the stands. They are cheering, waving purple flags, each with a silver half-moon, and holding up signs that read Stone 200, Tia 0.

Tia and Stone walk toward the fighters' mat. Their trainers walk beside them. Tia is a wearing a black bodysuit with a Gold B on the front. Trailing from the B are gold flames that spiral around her waist, her hips, and down her left leg. Stone is wearing a purple bodysuit. Dole is written through a silver half-moon on the back of the bodysuit.

TIA: *(She notices Stone and whispers to Coffus.)* What is it that he is doing with his face? Why is he showing me his teeth?

COFFUS: *(looking at Stone)* Stupid man! I've seen pictures of such behavior. It's called *smiling. (turning to Tia)* It's just a show of uncontrolled emotion. You'll have no trouble defeating the likes of him.

TIA: *(putting hand over heart)* When I saw him smile— as you call it—I felt something strange.

COFFUS: *(shaking head)* You are just anxious to fight.

(Attention moves to Stone and Ink.)

STONE: *(pointing at Dolian fans)* Just look at all of them, Ink! Somehow, they all managed to find a way here, even my mother and my sister.

INK: *(smiling)* This contest means a lot to our people.

STONE: *(thumbs up, waving to fans)* DOLE! DOLE! DOLE!

(Fans join in the chanting: DOLE! DOLE! DOLE!)

INK: *(yelling)* It's time, Stone. Put on your temple discs.

(Coffus and Tia stand.)

COFFUS: It's time, Tia. Put on your temple discs.

(Stone and Tia walk onto the mat and pick up their swords. Stone looks at the shouting Dolian fans. The thought board flashes that his positron level is 2500. Tia snarls at Stone. Her level is 2000.)

INK: *(hands cupped around mouth, calling to Stone)* Don't forget our plan. Make her think Dolian.

(Stone and Tia stand facing each other. Coffus and Ink sit in chairs at each end of the mat.)

ANNOUNCER: Let round one begin.

(A buzzer sounds. Tia and Stone exchange laser fire.)

ANNOUNCER: Right away, Tia takes Stone's ankle for 20 points.

(Stone flinches. Tia's thought board flashes Bast, *then switches to* smile.*)*

ANNOUNCER: Tia's losing power. Stone strikes her throat for twenty points. Tia recovers at once, spins around, and hits both of Stone's kidneys. Tia's score is now at 60.

(Stone's thought board reads She's good!*)*

ANNOUNCER: Stone recovers and strikes Tia's knee. Tia doesn't miss a beat, though, hitting Stone's left shoulder. Score now: Stone 40, Tia 80.

(Tia's thought board reads Fool. *Buzzer sounds to end Round One.)*

ANNOUNCER: That's the end of Round One. The score: Tia 80, Stone 40.

STONE: *(shouting to Tia)* Hey! You're good!

TIA: *(stunned)* What?

(Tia and Stone leave their swords in the middle of the mat and run to opposite sides.)

INK: *(rubbing Stone's shoulders)* You're doing fine, Stone.

STONE: *(looking at Tia)* She's incredible. She can spin and jump faster than I can blink.

INK: Stick with our plan, Stone. Just stick with our plan.

(Ink continues rubbing Stone's shoulders. Coffus talks with Tia.)

COFFUS: Eighty points in less than two minutes. It won't be long now. *(looking at Tia's face)* You aren't listening to me.

TIA: *(staring at Stone)* He told me I was good.

COFFUS: You are, best in the galaxy. *(glaring at Stone)*

(The buzzer sounds. Tia runs to the mat and picks up her sword.)

STONE: *(He runs to Tia and grabs her hand.)* You are the most beautiful Baston I have ever seen.

ANNOUNCER: I don't know what that handshake was about, but it surely shook up Tia. She's struggling to regain control. Check out that thought board. It's screaming *beautiful*, and her positron level is dropping. Stone's in the match, though. He just took Tia's ankle and both shoulders. Would you look at that? Tia's thought board is flashing *Mother*. What is going on?

(The crowd gasps at the word Mother.*)*

ANNOUNCER: Tia might as well go home with the positron level she's got now, a mere 200. Stone just hit her stomach, both kidneys, and leaped into the air for two megastrikes. He needs one more megastrike to put an end to this most unusual contest.

(Buzzer sounds to end Round Two.)

ANNOUNCER: That ends Round Two. Score: Stone 160, Tia 80.

(Tia drops her sword and walks slowly to her chair.)

COFFUS: *(furious)* What in the name of Bast was going on out there?

TIA: *(dazed)* He told me I was beautiful. He smiled constantly. *(sharply)* I wasn't prepared for this kind of behavior, Coffus. What does it mean?

COFFUS: *(teeth clenched)* All Bastons are beautiful! We are designed that way. That clown, on the other hand, is backward and unpredictable. Don't let his foolish chatter break your concentration.

TIA: *(eyes lowered)* I like what he said, Coffus.

COFFUS: *(losing patience)* May I remind you that if you do not regain your hatred of that fool, you will be banished this very day?

TIA: *(She straightens and glares at Stone.)* I can do this, Coffus. I'm ready.

(Attention shifts to Ink and Stone.)

STONE: *(smiling)* It's working, Ink! *(looking at Tia)* But it's working too well.

INK: *(rubbing Stone's shoulders)* What do you mean?

STONE: If she doesn't make at least one more strike, they'll kill her.

INK: So? She's just another Baston. She's not even real!

STONE: Yes, she is, Ink, and I think I'm reminding her of it.

INK: *(puzzled)* What are you saying?

STONE: I've touched something in her mind, Ink, something those unfeeling Bastons thought they had erased. *(standing)* Ink, I'm going to let her hit one of my microshields.

INK: *(He screams.)* WHAT?

STONE: Just one, Ink. I promise.

(Buzzer sounds. Tia and Stone walk onto the mat, eyes glued to each other. Stone fires several times but purpose-fully misses.)

ANNOUNCER: It's Round Three, and the action is getting weird already. Stone's standing there like a statue firing in the wind, and his positron level is at 4000. No fighter in his right mind passes up a 4000. Maybe his thought board can give us a clue.

(Stone's thought board flashes Don't beat her.*)*

TIA: *(confused, then screaming)* You're more foolish than I thought, Moon Man!

ANNOUNCER: I have to agree with Tia at this point. Stone's out of it. With her positron level back up, Tia just unloaded a direct hit to Stone's right knee. That brings her score to 100. But wait, now she's slowing down. This is one for the books. Tia's thought board is flashing *thank you,* and . . . and . . . would you look at that? Tia is smiling!

COFFUS: *(screaming)* What's going on? Rub that smile off your face and fire!

ANNOUNCER: Maybe it's a computer mistake. Maybe it's my eyes, but at the same time that Tia smiled, her positron level shot to 3000. She's firing nonstop now, and Stone's in a panic. Tia's got his throat, his stomach, his right shoulder, and two megastrikes over his heart. One more megastrike, and the gold is hers.

(Dolian fans scream louder than ever. Stone's mother and sister are the loudest.)

TIA: *(losing patience with the screaming, yells to Stone)* Hey, who are those women? Make them be quiet.

STONE: *(very angry)* That's my family! Too bad you don't have a mother to scream for you!

ANNOUNCER: I think we've got our sword fight back, ladies and gentlemen. Stone looks like he could kill someone, and, well, you can see Tia's thought board. Positron level at 3000, but I don't understand that *Mother, Mother, Mother* we keep seeing.

(Buzzer sounds.)

ANNOUNCER: End of Round Three. Score tied at 160.

(Stone and Tia go to their seats.)

TIA: *(screaming at Coffus)* Can't at least one Baston support me during this fight? Why do they all sit there like robots?

(Coffus, wide-eyed and confused, shakes his head from side to side. Attention shifts to Stone and Ink.)

STONE: I don't know what's going on, Ink. She was supposed to be confused by the kindness, not decide she liked it. I thought she would experience a happy emotion, then feel guilty about it, and lose positrons. Instead, she's changing, Ink. And the happy feelings are giving her power.

INK: You've got a fight to win, Stone, and it's a real one now.

(Buzzer sounds. Tia and Stone explode onto the mat.)

ANNOUNCER: Well, fans, we've seen it all today. Tia and Stone are at a standoff. It could go either way. They both need one megastrike to win the gold. The fighting is fierce. Both are firing nonstop. Now get this: Stone has started to smile again. And believe it or not, Tia has just started to smile again, too. WAIT, what's this? Tia's hit! It's all over! Stone has found his mark. The gold will go to the champion from Dole. The Baston will settle for the silver.

(The crowd goes wild with noise.)

(Lights out.)

ACT FOUR

The Baston Olympics training tower practice room. Tia is seated in the middle of the fighters' pad, her sword resting at her side. She's staring into space. Coffus enters, picks up Tia's sword, and motions for her to rise for practice. She does not move.

COFFUS: *(slightly angry)* You won the silver. You can compete again. Let's get to work.

(Tia does not move. She does not look at Coffus.)

COFFUS: *(angry)* You allowed yourself to be troubled by that fool Dolian. You caused your own downfall.

TIA: *(glaring at Coffus)* Yes, I will compete again, and I will walk away with a gold medal, too.

(Coffus and Tia put on their temple discs and start to fight.)

TIA: *(striking Coffus again and again)* Too bad you can't see my thought board, Coffus. I'll tell you what it says: *Bast bad; Dole good.* How do you like that,

173

Coffus? Oh, that's right, Bastons don't LIKE anything.

*(Coffus falls to the ground. He is wide-eyed and speech-
less.)*

TIA: *(looking down at Coffus)* Yes, I will be competing
again, Coffus, but not for Bast.

COFFUS: Tia, you're insane! What are you babbling
about?

TIA: I'm leaving to become a fighter for some other
planet, or maybe a moon . . . maybe even Dole.

COFFUS: *(He stands and aims sword at Tia.)* Why? Just
tell me why?

TIA: Because I learned some things about myself,
about my *real* self, Coffus. I learned that I have a
brain that can think for itself. I learned I have a
heart that *feels.* So there! *(Tia makes a giant, unex-
pected leap, striking Coffus's most difficult
microshield, one planted in the top of his head.)*

READING FOR UNDERSTANDING

Act One

1. What is Dole? Why do the Dolians live there?
2. How does Tia feel about the Dolians? Why?
3. How is the doctor's office on Dole different from the one on Bast? What do these differences suggest about their peoples' ways of thinking?
4. What emotions do Dolians feel that Bastons do not?

Act Two

5. What does Coffus say about Dolians?
6. What does Tia say about winning the gold medal. Why does she feel this way?
7. What happens when Tia's thought board flashes *Mother*? What happens when it flashes *Bast*?

Act Three

8. What does Stone's mother notice about the fans in the stands? How does Stone's sister explain the fans' reaction?
9. What do the runners, swimmers, and basketball players look like?
10. How are the athletes from Dole different from the other athletes?
11. What happens to the sword fighter from Bast? Why?

Act Four

12. According to Coffus, what made Tia lose?
13. According to Tia, what would her thought board say?
14. Will Tia compete again? Whom will she fight for?

RESPONDING TO THE PLAY

1. Throughout the play, we learn about how people on Bast and Dole think and act. Where would you rather live, on Bast or on Dole? Write a diary entry explaining your choice.
2. At the end of Act Three, Stone's positron level is at 4000. Why is his level so high? Do you think that positive thoughts are more powerful than negative thoughts? Defend your point of view in a paragraph.

REVIEWING VOCABULARY

Match each word on the left with the correct definition on the right.

1. galaxy	**a.** sudden fall
2. eliminated	**b.** device that gives off beams
3. artificial	**c.** small, sharp knife
4. laser	**d.** removed
5. scalpel	**e.** large group of stars
6. downfall	**f.** not natural

THINKING CRITICALLY

1. Why do you think that Tia feels the way she does about Dolians? How does Stone show pity for Tia? How does he show courage?
2. How is the training different for the two doctors? How are they different in the way they look at life?
3. What does the play reveal about the power of positive thinking and emotions? What does the play suggest about negative thinking and emotions?
4. How has Tia changed by the end of the play? What has she learned about herself?

WRITING PROJECTS

1. Imagine that you have been hired to write a sequel to *A Clash of Wills*. Together with two or three classmates, make an outline for a sequel play. Your play outline may discuss some of the following issues: Would Tia and Stone continue to be laser sword fighters? Would they meet again? Would Tia leave Bast?

2. Imagine that you are a laser sword fighter from Dole competing in the Galactic Olympics. Write a report about your experiences. Describe in your report what you look like and how you think.

The Green Computer

Chuck Haines

What would you do if faced with a computer that is out of control? Pull the plug? Turn the machine off? Sounds simple, doesn't it?

In The Green Computer, *scientists of the future have built a "molecular" computer. It has "living" parts. Its "brain" is made out of plant material. Proteins have replaced computer chips.*

The computer has been installed in a research lab on the moon. There, daring experiments with plants from Earth are underway.

Then the scientists realize that things are going wrong. All too late, they find that they have lost control of the computer. Read on to find out what happens in this play about science and nature.

VOCABULARY WORDS

saturate (SATCH-eh-rayt) to cause to be completely soaked
❖ Before I go on vacation, I will *saturate* the plants with water.

accessory (ak-SES-uhr-ee) additional; secondary
❖ It was so bright in the room that we didn't bother to switch on the *accessory* lights.

delirious (dih-LIHR-ee-uhs) raving; out of one's mind
❖ Her fever was so high that she was *delirious*.

machete (muh-SHEHT-ee) heavy, large-bladed knife
❖ She cut her way through the jungle with a *machete*.

KEY WORDS

botanist (BAHT-uhn-ihst) a specialist in plants and plant life
❖ The *botanist* was an expert on plant growth.

cloned (klohnd) created by moving genetic material from one organism to another
❖ Scientists are finding that many life forms can be *cloned*.

luciferin (loo-SIHF-uhr-ihn) light-producing substance
❖ The plants produced more light because Betty put more *luciferin* in their feeding water.

metabolic (meht-uh-BAHL-ihk) related to the way in which all living things process food
❖ He was on a strict diet for his *metabolic* problem.

toxins (TAHKS-ihnz) poisonous substances
❖ The *toxins* are so powerful that contact with your skin will result in severe burns.

CHARACTERS

Marsha Hart, *chief botanist, Greenhouse Unit, Moon Base I*

Betty Fry, *assistant botanist*

Ed Minden, *chief electronic engineer*

"Doc" Conrad Han, *M.D., space physiologist*

Alex Brown, *computer scientist*

SETTING

Act One

Scene 1

Greenhouse at Moon Base I in the year 2017. A digital army clock reads 1100 hours.

Scene 2

Storage room at the Greenhouse. Another clock reads 1200 hours.

Act Two

Scene 1

The Molecular Computing Room, next to the Greenhouse. The clock reads 1203 hours.

Scene 2

Greenhouse. The clock reads 1208 hours.

Scene 3

Greenhouse. The clocks reads 2355 hours.

ACT ONE, SCENE 1

*A **large greenhouse area** at the first experimental research station on the moon. The room is crowded with healthy plants. Against one wall, corn, beans, and squash are growing under a sign that reads, "The Native American Three Sister Plants." Tropical plants,*

181

such as banana trees and coconut palms, are growing in planters near the far left.

Thousands of stars shine through the glass walls. At the same time, all of the plants are glowing with a strange fluorescent light. Marsha Hart, a slender, middle-aged woman in a white lab coat, is speaking into a small hand-held recorder.)

MARSHA: Eleven hundred hours. Project Plantpower proceeding ahead of schedule. Installation of moon bases on dark side of moon will be illuminated by plants during third phase of project—

(Betty enters. She is about Marsha's age and wearing an identical lab coat.)

BETTY: Oh! Sorry to interrupt. You asked me to come?

MARSHA: Go tell Bill we have another water leak or else the computer timing switch isn't shutting off.

BETTY: He's sick today. Judy and Mike are also sick with stomach problems.

MARSHA: Then call Facilities. See if Ed can come to check the lines again. It's the third time in two days that we've had this same problem. Tell Ed the computer lines may be getting wet and shorting out.

BETTY: *(She walks over to the central desk, flips a switch, and then speaks into a microphone.)* Ed, we have another water problem. Yes, another leak.

MARSHA: Tell him the timing mechanism might need to be adjusted. Whatever the problem is, tell Ed we need to have it fixed as soon as possible.

BETTY: Marsha thinks it's the computer timing mechanism. Oh. OK. See you then. *(She turns off the switch* *and looks at Marsha.)* Ed said it can't be the timing regulator. They just put a new one in. It must be the water valves themselves, something sticking open.

MARSHA: I don't think so, I check those every day. When did that rash on your hands develop, Betty?

BETTY: Three days ago. It seems to be spreading, but I got some salve from Doc. He said that it looked like a poison ivy rash.

MARSHA: What else did Ed say?

BETTY: He said that first he had to finish some work next door in the computer room. I guess those processing units are giving them trouble again.

MARSHA: *(She walks over to the work area.)* Why are these plants dying? I just fed them Monday.

BETTY: There's a couple over there that are also losing their leaves. I noticed the problem yesterday when the light from their leaves dimmed.

MARSHA: I can't figure out why those plants are dimming, while the others are thriving and glowing.

(pause)

BETTY: I put more luciferin in their feeding water to intensify their light production. I guess we have a metabolic problem because the light intensity diminished.

MARSHA: Do you think they're getting too much water?

BETTY: I haven't seen the soil test from the computer printout yet. Do you think . . . *(She stops as Ed walks into the Greenhouse area. He is a tall, sturdy, older man with brown hair, graying at the temples.)*

MARSHA: Ed, we seem to have a number of problems.

ED: So what's wrong now?

MARSHA: Either the watering mechanism is leaking or the computer is turning on the water too often.

ED: How do you know that?

MARSHA: *(She points to a page with statistics on a clipboard hanging on the wall.)* There's the log. We've been measuring the water saturation levels for the last two months. It's still too high. Today, it was eighty-nine percent. Yesterday, it was eighty-eight percent. We have to keep setting the timing regulator back to water every fifteen hours.

ED: You shouldn't have to touch the timing regulator. It's controlled by the program.

MARSHA: For some reason, it is automatically resetting every four hours. Bill replaced the timing unit two weeks ago. He said the old one was still as good as new. Maybe it's the new processing unit for the computer that regulates the timing.

ED: I don't think so. *(He looks around and rubs his eyes.)* Say, isn't it a lot brighter in here?

MARSHA: The plants have set a new record for light output. The potatoes and beans are going off the scale for light production. The gourd plants are a close second. Even the corn is emitting record levels. I think we are finally producing enough light so we can shut down several banks of batteries. We haven't had time to analyze the data because Judy and Mike are sick.

ED: Well, let me look at the regulator. We'll see what's wrong, if anything. *(He walks over to the water connection unit.)* Hey, Marsha, this gourd vine has grown around the connector.

MARSHA: What are you talking about?

ED: *(He looks astonished.)* Wow, look at all the light coming from that vine! Is that normal?

MARSHA: Let me see. Betty, go talk to Mike and Judy at their quarters. Ask them if they noted anything strange about the water control mechanism.

BETTY: What do you mean, "anything strange"?

MARSHA: Just ask if they noticed the vines growing in this back section where the water regulator is connected to the computer. They're the last ones who worked in this area.

BETTY: OK. I'll be right back. *(She leaves the room.)*

MARSHA: Ed, something very unusual is going on here. These vines shouldn't be over here. Look at the gourd and the passionflower. The buffalo gourd is growing all over the mechanism. Turn off the accessory lights. Let's see how much light they're producing.

ED: OK. *(He turns off the lights.)*

MARSHA: Wow! The light production is tremendous. We don't even need the accessory lights. These plants are growing too fast. They've spread out of their area. Their light production is at levels we've never seen before. They must be processing their luciferin more efficiently.

ED: I thought there was a limit to the amount of luciferin these plants could absorb.

BETTY: When we first started extracting luciferin from fireflies, that was true. But the synthetic luciferin is different. We put it in the soil, and the plants eat it like candy. We've been regulating the luciferin at very low levels because the plant roots take it up so fast.

MARSHA: Our plants here on the moon are genetically cloned with luciferase, the enzyme that breaks down luciferin in both fireflies and plants. The light is produced when luciferase breaks down a chemical bond in luciferin. But we've never seen anything like this.

ED: How could these vines move into the area so fast? Look here, the leader of this gourd vine is inside the seal on the wall. What's going on here? *(He is beginning to sound worried.)*

MARSHA: I don't know. I hadn't noticed.

ED: I just left Alex. We've been having some problems with the molecular computer. It started when we installed the new molecular processing units two months ago. I'm not sure, but this could be serious. The computer now controls most of our life-support systems here.

MARSHA: What's the problem?

ED: Well, we used the plant material you gave us to prepare the new processing unit. We purified the carbohydrates and proteins from the plant material. It's the first time we've built a computer processor from our own plant material here on the moon. In the past, Base Station always sent us their refined plant material for adding new processing units. Your plant material is supposed to be the same, right?

MARSHA: I think so, at least from what I understand

about molecular computers. I thought this new computer of yours could use any plant material to perform the computing functions.

ED: Yes. But the parallel units are working too fast and too frequently.

MARSHA: What do you mean?

ED: Well, one of the units is processing some type of information on its own. It is coming up with some weird information that we never gave it.

MARSHA: That's impossible.

ED: I know, but over the last forty-eight hours, the central monitor reported sixteen hours of extra processing time going through the unit. The systems check showed that the trouble was with the new unit. When we checked out the unit, we didn't recognize any of the codes it was using. Alex said that this has been happening for more than a month. He thought the unit was performing system checks on itself. So he didn't worry about it.

MARSHA: Then the molecular computer is processing information that you don't recognize?

ED: *(more urgently)* There's more. We ran a program to decipher the information. It came up blank. "Unknown logic" was the only response the test gave.

MARSHA: Unknown logic?

ED: The test indicated that the new processing unit is using an unknown logic system, an unusual code that has no explanation. Alex's trying to decipher the information with other system tests right now.

MARSHA: Ed, this doesn't make sense.

ED: Compared to old-fashioned microchip computers, our new molecular computers, made from carbohydrates, nucleic acids, and proteins, are really simple. These don't have to be programmed to store information.

MARSHA: Why not?

ED: Because they don't have to switch on and off. Their molecules just organize themselves into different patterns when they are connected to electrical signals.

MARSHA: Then that's why molecular computers work so fast.

ED: Yes, they can process information faster than any known microchip. You could almost say that they have a mind of their own. They have life in them. Well, anyway, I told Alex that I would be next door working on your water problem if anything new came up.

(Betty walks into the Greenhouse, looking concerned.)

BETTY: Bill and Judy are really sick. They have a rash all over their bodies and can't keep food or liquids down. Doc's with them now. He says something about food poisoning and poison ivy.

MARSHA: There's no poison ivy here. I wonder what they picked up. Did you ask them about the plants near the water regulator?

BETTY: Yes. They said they noted it in the log and pulled the leader vines out of the area. They also set up a small vine rail to stop the leader vines from coming into the area.

MARSHA: That's odd. The vine rails were on the ground

when I came in this morning. I picked them up and set them back in the storage. *(She scratches her hand.)* Anything else?

BETTY: Judy was a little delirious. She kept saying the words *light* and *water*.

MARSHA: Hmm. Ed just turned the accessory lights out. Look around you. *(waving her arms around the room)* All this light is coming from the plants, especially the light from this bunch of vines around the water regulator.

ED: What's the name of this vine?

MARSHA: Oh, that's buffalo gourd from the Earth's tall grass prairies. These vines can reach one hundred twenty-five feet. Some of the roots on the old plants can grow as big as a person.

ED: Those vines must be sixty or seventy feet long. Look how thick they are.

MARSHA: This plant is only four years old, but it's really growing fast.

ED: *(He looks startled.)* Say, this vine is even brighter than that other one.

BETTY: Marsha, I haven't turned up the luciferin feeding regulator. In fact, I haven't even checked it for a while. I'd better take a look right now.

(She walks over to the side of the room.)

BETTY: The valve is set correctly. The printout on the recorder indicates that it's been releasing the luciferin right on schedule. The amount is correct, also.

MARSHA: Get the luciferin probe. Take a measurement in the soil over there by the water valve where all those vines are growing.

ED: *(looking very worried and speaking rapidly)* Something is terribly wrong here, Marsha. First, the computer has been processing information that we can't identify. Second, your Greenhouse Unit has two people sick with some mysterious disease. Third, your plants are growing into the cracks in the wall near the plumbing and . . .

BETTY AND MARSHA: *(Both interrupt him at the same time.)* What?

ED: Look at these vines. They're all over the wall. Look down here where the water and conduit pipes run into the Greenhouse. Your darn plants seem to be packing themselves into the space between the pipes and the wall. *(frustrated and impatient)* How often do you check this area out, Marsha?

MARSHA: I guess it's been about three weeks. We've been very busy preparing the new area for more plants.

ED: Have you checked out that enclosed area in the back of storage? You know, where the computer makes the connection with the water and feeding mechanisms.

MARSHA: No. That's your job, remember?

ED: Let's check it out.

BETTY: Marsha, the luciferin level in the soil is forty percent above normal. That's really strange. *(speaking to herself while she scratches her rash)* I wonder how so much luciferin got into the soil.

MARSHA: Come on, Betty. Help us check out the wiring area in the storage area. We'll take one problem at a time. And please try to stop scratching. You'll only make it worse. *(They walk out through the side door.)*

(The stage goes dark.)

ACT ONE, SCENE 2

The storage area next to the Greenhouse. Marsha, Betty, and Ed enter the area, which is crowded with pots, shovels, and other tools that are lined up on racks.

MARSHA: Ed, do you have the key to the engineering room in back?

ED: I've got a master key. *(He walks through the storage area, then unlocks and opens the back door to the engineering room and looks in. He rushes back to them, covering his eyes.)* We have to do something. This is getting scary. Look at all that light. Those vines! They're so bright! *(turning on Marsha and yelling)* Where are they coming from? Your buffalo gourd vines are covering all my wires. You're supposed to be the expert botanist, Marsha. What are you going to do about it?

MARSHA: *(taking two steps back, looking blank, and stuttering)* Ed . . . Ed, I'm just as surprised as you are. I have no idea how the vines got in there or what they are doing here.

ED: *(ignoring Marsha's confusion and speaking to Betty)* Let's check the computer wire connections. *(Ed and Betty go back to look into the engineering area, then quickly return.)* The connectors are completely covered with the vines. We have to try to cut them back.

Betty, could you get us a couple of pruning knives so we can remove the vines? *(Marsha stands by, trying to regain her composure.)*

ED: *(He follows Betty to the tool rack as Dr. Conrad Han walks up to Marsha. He scratches the back of his head, thinking.)* Hi, Doc.

DOC: Mike, Bill, and Judy are severely ill. Their lab tests indicate a high level of two totally different plant toxins in their blood. This is amazing. *(He hands a copy of the test results to Marsha.)*

MARSHA: What do you mean, Doc? *(While listening to the doctor, she looks over the test results.)*

DOC: They have all the symptoms of food poisoning. Tests indicate that their skin rash must be caused by poison ivy.

MARSHA: *(astounded, but back in control)* Hold on, Doc. There's no poison ivy here. That's absolutely impossible. Your tests are showing toxins from plants we don't have here at the research station.

BETTY: How sick are they, Doc?

DOC: *(He looks down at the floor and shakes his head.)* It's very serious. And Bill has the same thing. There's no way to counteract the toxin levels in their blood. These toxins cause a slow, painful death. *(He looks directly at Marsha.)* Did Bill spend any time in the Greenhouse Unit recently?

BETTY: Bill and Mike were preparing new soil and doing some planting for the last couple of days. They also talked about cutting down some vines.

DOC: *(still looking at Marsha)* Is it possible that the

192

plants here are somehow producing these toxins?

MARSHA: I'm not certain of anything anymore. *(She glares at Ed and waves her arms in the air in frustration.)* Ed's telling me that our fancy molecular computer is making calculations that he and Alex can't interpret. It just doesn't make any sense.

ED: Uhh . . . Well, I think . . .

MARSHA: *(interrupting as she locks her eyes on Ed)* The plants and the computer are linked in some way. They are creating something we can only guess at.

BETTY: Why don't we temporarily disconnect the computer from the Greenhouse?

MARSHA: Let's also see if we can clear out the vines and disconnect the water and feeding lines.

DOC: I've got to get back to my patients. Don't handle these plants until we find the source of the toxins. It's too dangerous. Perhaps Ed and Alex can disconnect everything from the computer room. What do you think, Ed?

ED: Let's go try it. *(Marsha and Doc follow Ed as he rushes out of the storage room, while Betty stays behind and looks at the plants.)*

(The stage goes dark.)

ACT TWO, SCENE 1

The Molecular Computing Room. The walls are lined with all types of computer instruments, flashing lights, knobs, and computer tape machines and circular tape heads. A digital army clock reads 1203 hours. On the wall next to the clock is a plaque that states in large let-

ters, "SITE OF THE FIRST LIVING COMPUTER." Alex sits behind a huge green keyboard and an eerie green computer screen under a gigantic hanging sweet-potato plant. He looks up as Ed runs in, out of breath, followed by Marsha.

ED: Quick. We must disengage all computer systems regulating the Greenhouse. We've got to kill those plants before they spread any more poison.

ALEX: What?

ED: Just do it. I'll explain later. There's no time.

ALEX: But . . .

ED: *(He pushes Alex away from the keyboard and sits down.)* Get out of the way. I designed this thing. I know what I'm doing. *(He types in a code.)* Here we go . . . *(Five seconds pass.)* System access to environmental management. *(Another few seconds pass.)* Oh, no! I can't interrupt the system. The processing unit has me blocked out.

ALEX: That's impossible!

ED: This unit is bypassing commands. We have to try to stop it.

ALEX: Try the back-door security password.

ED: *(smiles)* It's working. Now I can shut down the new processor and still save the rest of the computer.

MARSHA: Wait! Before you kill it, take a look at the data it collected on soil and light for the last month. I've been too busy to check that computer data.

ED: *(He types in some commands, then looks at the printer.)* There it is.

MARSHA: *(She picks up the printout and looks at it.)* This isn't what I expected. We've got to get back to the Greenhouse. Betty might be trying to cut the plants.

(The stage goes dark.)

ACT TWO, SCENE 2

The Greenhouse. Marsha runs in and finds Betty chopping at the passionflower and gourd vines with a machete.

BETTY: Grab another machete and help me. We've got to kill these passionflower and buffalo gourd plants.

MARSHA: No, Betty! NO! Stop it! It's not those vines. Their roots are producing the toxins because they're threatened by their new environment.

ED: What?

MARSHA: The data shows that some of the plants are reacting to the increased light from the three sister plants. The corn, beans, and squash are growing faster than we expected and making much more light.

BETTY: Do you mean that the light has something to do with the toxins?

MARSHA: I think so. I just saw the computer printout on the soil tests and light levels. It shows that the soil around the buffalo gourd and passionflower have the highest level of toxins.

ED: But why are they making toxins?

MARSHA: Putting the plants on the moon has totally

changed their environment, and their survival is threatened. They want to protect themselves. So the passionflower and buffalo gourd made toxins in self-defense. That's how all plants survive.

ED: How did Mike, Bill, and Judy get poisoned?

MARSHA: The entire plant makes the toxins. Bill and Mike absorbed the toxins through the skin on their hands when they touched the vines. Judy absorbed the toxins when she touched the soil around the roots.

ED: What can we do now?

MARSHA: It's simple. We just have to move the buffalo gourd and the passionflower to a place where there's less light. That will give them the message that they don't have to produce toxins anymore.

ED: But what went wrong with the computer?

MARSHA: Ed, don't the biomolecules in the green computer depend upon water to function?

BETTY: Of course! Now I understand. The connection has to be the roots. The water conducts the information back and forth between the computer and the plant roots.

ED: What in the world are you talking about?

MARSHA: Ed, the water is acting like an electrical wire that connects the green computer to the plants. The roots use water to communicate with the computer.

BETTY: Somehow, the plants and the computer share a common ancestor biomolecule. It's as if they are brother and sister. Now, they speak the same language, and they're helping each other.

ED: So when your vines started growing around the water pipes and the electrical wires, they connected themselves to the computer's central processing unit. That's its brain.

MARSHA: And the root is the brain of the plant.

ED: We can't shut down the computer. We'll all die.

BETTY: We have no way to drain the water lines.

ED: We must destroy the roots. Where are the shovels?

BETTY: Over there, on the rack. *(Ed gets the shovels.)*

MARSHA: You have to wear gloves and surgical masks. If you inhale any of the toxins, Ed, you might die. Remember Judy and Mike. *(Betty goes to the supply shelf and returns with the gloves and masks.)* Ed, you start over there on the buffalo gourd root. *(They put on the masks and gloves and dig for the next few minutes.)*

ED: *(He groans.)* How deep are these roots, anyway?

MARSHA: Just keep digging.

(The stage goes dark.)

ACT TWO, SCENE 3

Greenhouse. The clock reads 2355. Doc has joined Ed in digging up the enormous buffalo gourd roots. Both men are wearing masks and gloves and sweating and groaning. Marsha and Betty are examining the remains of all the roots that they have dug up. Marsha is standing in front of a thick, four-foot-long root. The women are wearing gloves only.

MARSHA: Ed, aren't you finished with that last root yet?

197

ED: You didn't tell me they were this big and tough. Didn't you say these were only four years old?

MARSHA: How do you think the buffalo survived for all those years? They needed a strong, tough plant to eat. They even scratched their backs with the leaves.

ED: Very interesting, Marsha. Maybe we should all work on destroying these roots.

DOC: Well, we have to be careful. The toxin in this buffalo gourd root—

BETTY: Wait. Marsha, listen. It's so quiet. And it's getting darker in here. What happened to the blower in the ventilation system?

MARSHA: I don't know, but the plants are losing their ability to produce light. Is it possible that . . . *(Alex enters in hysteria, jumping up and down and waving his arms.)*

ALEX: Ed! Come quick! The computer's down! It just shut down. I don't know what happened. The life-support systems are shutting down all over the base. Bill and Mike are—

ED AND DOC: *(both stand waist deep in the buffalo gourd hole. They look down at the root, then up at each other.)* Oh, no! *(The clock stops and the lights go out.)*

READING FOR UNDERSTANDING

The following paragraphs summarize the play. Decide which of the words below the paragraph best fits in each blank. Write your answers on a separate sheet of paper.

Marsha Hart is the chief **(1)**_____ in the Greenhouse Unit of the first research station. Suddenly, she faces several new problems. Her assistant Betty develops a strange **(2)**_____. The water levels for the plants are too **(3)**_____. Some plants are emitting record levels of **(4)**_____.

Ed, the chief **(5)**_____, says that the molecular **(6)**_____ is also having problems. This special computer has been made from plant **(7)**_____ such as proteins. Now the computer is processing **(8)**_____ that the scientists can't identify. In addition, Bill and Judy are sick with a mysterious **(9)**_____.

Marsha, Betty, and Ed check the storage **(10)**_____. They find that the vines have **(11)**_____ tremendously. They now completely cover the computer's wire **(12)**_____. Doc warns them against contact with the highly dangerous plant **(13)**_____. Ed decides that all the computer **(14)**_____ regulating the Greenhouse must be disconnected. Betty tries to destroy the vines with a **(15)**_____. Marsha explains that the **(16)**_____ used to feed the plants has acted like an electrical wire. This allowed the plants' roots to send the computer **(17)**_____. As the researchers work to destroy the roots, the computer fails, and the life-support systems all over the **(18)**_____ shut down.

Words: *material, botanist, light, haywire, base, connectors, grown, engineer, high, area, disease, computer,* *machete, toxins, rash, information, water, systems*

RESPONDING TO THE PLAY

1. Did you find the events of this play believable? Do you think they could really happen in the future? Write a letter to the author giving your opinion.

2. What do you think will happen after the end of the play? Will the characters die, or will they find a way out of their problem? Discuss your ideas with a small group of classmates.

REVIEWING VOCABULARY

1. After the flood, the basement became *saturated*, or **(a)** dried out **(b)** emptied of furniture **(c)** completely soaked.

2. A *botanist* is a specialist in **(a)** aerospace **(b)** endangered species **(c)** plants.

3. It is wise to avoid contact with *toxins* because they are **(a)** poisonous **(b)** addictive **(c)** razor sharp.

4. If a person is *delirious*, he or she is **(a)** sleepy **(b)** raving **(c)** extremely hungry.

5. If an item is classified as an *accessory* part for a machine, we know that it is **(a)** essential **(b)** secondary **(c)** very expensive.

6. A *machete* is a large **(a)** computer **(b)** knife **(c)** plant.

THINKING CRITICALLY

1. According to Ed, what are some of the advantages of a molecular, or green, computer, as opposed to "old-fashioned microchip computers"?

2. According to Marsha, why did the vine roots start to produce toxins?